False

Security

David C. Koch
Christine L. Koch

The Aerospace Trust Press
www.aerospacetrust.com

Published by
The Aerospace Trust Press
3465 S. Arlington Road
Suite E-157
Akron, OH 44312
www.aerospacetrust.com

Printed in the United States of America

Cover designed by
Caler&Company
Akron, Ohio

ISBN 0-9726991-1-2

This book is dedicated to *The Wright Brothers, Charles Lindbergh, Antoine de Saint-Exupéry, Juan Trippe, Werner von Braun* and all the other dreamers who have provided us with a vision of a better future through air and space transportation. It is also dedicated to the current and future visionaries who are proving that the sky is no longer the limit.

Contents

f

Pre-Flight Briefing

"False security is just as good as real security,
right up to the time it's tested."
                              Capt. David C. Koch

Ladies and gentlemen this is your captain speaking—literally. You are about to embark on a journey that is guaranteed to be _shocking, frightening, interesting, enlightening, optimistic and sometimes humorous._ You can expect a few bumps along the way, but I promise a happy landing in an air-travel future that you can help to create.

This expedition, like all really good adventures, will take you places that you have never been before. It will also show you the behind-the-scenes real world of air travel and some of the politics that come into play in establishing the level of safety and convenience that you experience while traveling by airline in the U.S. today. I'll even drag a skeleton out of the airline industry's closet—it's a *"doozy"*. I can assure you that I saw quite a few in the two decades that I flew as a pilot for United Airlines. And my extracurricular activities (e.g., pilot-union activist, special assistant to the president of United Airlines for Space Shuttle acquisition and others) provided me with a unique insight into the workings of a major airline.

This book will also give you a very close look at some air-travel problems that will cause you great concern. After reading it, I believe you will agree that your personal safety while flying aboard a U.S. airliner has been compromised beyond all reasonable limits. But take heart, this is also a story about a possible future that will fill you with optimism.

We will also visit the philosophical question: *"is false security just as good as real security?"* This is a question that I have been pondering for the past several years. I'll try to convince you, in a sometimes humorous manner, that it is—right up to the time it's tested.

If you are an air traveler, you are currently entrusting your very life to an airline system that you probably don't really know much about. If you live on the same planet as I do, I know that you have grave doubts about the real safety and security of the U.S. air-transportation system. This book will provide you with the facts that you need to make informed decisions about the air-travel solutions that you choose, and it will give you genuine hope for a better air-travel future.

The first ten chapters of *"False Security"* contain a fictional account of the experiences of one hapless air traveler who discovers the difference between false security and real security in a most poignant manner. Our intrepid adventurer also encounters a future that is far more positive than you may now believe possible.

I must emphasize, however, that the story in the first 10 chapters is *fictional*. I made the whole thing up. But like all fiction, the characters and events in the story are based upon composites of real people and actual events.

The future that I write about is purely a figment of my imagination. However, it is based upon thinking that I have come across in my study of forward thinkers like Werner von Braun, Buckminster Fuller and Robert Heinlein. I'll leave it up to you to make up your own mind about how *real* it can become.

Chapter 11, *"Just The Facts"*, offers a transition from our fictional world back into reality. I'll take you behind the scenes at the airlines to show you how airline politics really work. The facts presented in this chapter should confirm for you that certain parts of the fictional story presented in chapters 1 through 10 could be real. By the end of this chapter, you should be able to make up your mind about false security versus real security.

In Chapter 12, *"Flying Blind"*, we'll take a hard-nosed, non-fiction look at one of the major air-travel-related issues that you will encounter in our fictional story—*pilot impairment*. At least one aspect of this growing problem will shock you, and I believe it will fill you with indignation. For apparently, the airline industry has perpetrated a massive cover-up of the facts related to this problem.

As an air traveler, you have a right to know about the airline-industry problems that have an impact on your safety. This lack of candor on the part of airline managers may have already led to the loss of the lives of many innocent air travelers. After you read this chapter and give it careful consideration, I think you will agree that *SOMETHING MUST BE DONE.*

Chapter 13, *"Ascending Unto Heaven"*, provides you with a flight plan that will set you on a course to a better way to fly. I suggest that you study this flight plan particularly carefully. I can honestly say that I believe it will take you exactly where you want to go.

I had a great time writing this book. In the 37 years that I have been an aviation industry professional, I have always enjoyed sharing what I know about the industry with fellow air travelers. Contributing to the enjoyment of writing this book was the fact that I have co-written it with my wife, copilot, business partner and best friend, Christine. She and I have been flying together as professional pilots for the past 8 years. It was fun to apply our cockpit-resource-management skills to another field of endeavor.

In addition to writing a large portion of the book, Christine did virtually all of the intensive research that was needed to bring to you the latest information on the state of the airline industry. She also designed the layout for the book and type-set it. It is truly a blessing to have such a talented partner.

Christine and I believe that when you have finished reading the book, you will have a realistic basis for making safe air-travel decisions. You will also have the knowledge to secure (for yourself, and your loved ones) fast, convenient, safe and secure air travel. We're sure that you will also have discovered some new ideas. They might lead you to places you haven't even dreamed of yet. You will also have the means at your disposal to do something about the appalling decline in the U.S. airline industry. But most of all, we want you to come away from *"False Security"* with a clear view of the differences between *false security* and *real security*.

So, welcome aboard. Please, just sit back, relax and enjoy the flight.

David C. Koch
Blimp City, U.S.A
2002

Chapter 1: *"Aerial Odyssey"*

*"I fly because it releases my mind
from the tyranny of petty things."*

Antoine de Saint-Exupéry

You are wedged into seat 33D. It is unfortunately a center seat, on the right side, two-thirds of the way towards the back of the narrow-bodied MD-80. It's been a very long, frustrating day. You are barely aware of your surroundings as you hunch down in your cramped coach seat reading a paperback novel you picked up at the Dallas/Ft. Worth International Airport (DFW). You would have preferred to catch up on the day's news, but there isn't even enough room in your cramped quarters to allow you to open a newspaper.

You've been cooped up in these cattle-car-like surroundings for almost two hours now. No, make that over eight hours if you count all the delayed flights you've been on today. The second alcoholic beverage you just finished helped to lull you into a sense of serene security. You had given no thought to the fact that at typical airliner cabin altitudes, two drinks are equivalent to four on the ground; nor to the effect the resulting level of impairment may mean to you if something critical were to happen while you are aboard a jet airliner.

On your left, in the aisle seat, is a burly man who, by the looks of him, must have been a linebacker in his youth. He's overflowing the coach seat that was obviously designed for a much smaller person. Since the airplane left the gate at DFW, you've been jammed in next to him with your left leg and arm in intimate contact with his right side. The thought, let alone the actuality, of involuntarily rubbing up against someone you don't know for an extended period of time makes you very uncomfortable. The fact that he has been scratching himself vigorously for the last several minutes makes you want to ease away from him as much as possible.

Much to your chagrin, on your right is what appears to be a ten-year-old boy who has spent the entire trip wiggling around and playing "you're it" with his sister in the seat behind him—when they weren't fighting. Two babies towards the front of the narrow aluminum tube have been serenading each other for some time now. They must be horrified by the strange noises, vibrations and pressure changes. You can only pray that maybe next time their parents will know better than to subject them to such a terrifying experience.

The only saving grace in this aeronautical odyssey is the fact that you are now only about ten minutes from what will be your final landing of the day. It won't be long now before you'll be home enjoying a late-night cocktail with your spouse and looking in on your two kids who will hopefully be tucked in for the night. You're looking forward to the big hug you are going to give them when they wake up in the morning. You had missed that parental pleasure this morning because you had left home before they were awake. It sure will be nice to be home again. You feel like you've been gone for a week. Has it really only been since this morning?

This latest airline adventure of yours began yesterday afternoon when your boss told you to travel to Atlanta from your home in El Paso to meet with a very-important client. It would have to be a one-day trip because a top-level staff meeting was scheduled in the El Paso office for the day after. The only flight your travel agent could find that would work for you left this morning at 6 AM MST with a connection in Dallas that would require a one-hour layover in the DFW terminal. You knew that you just might have enough time to run the mile or so from your arrival gate to your departure gate—if everything went well. The connecting flight's scheduled arrival time in Atlanta was 1:13 PM EST. That would give you barely sufficient time to take a cab into the city center to meet with your client before you would have to rush back to The Hartsfield Atlanta International Airport (ATL) for your 5:36 PM EST flight home.

Of course, you'd be stopping in DFW again on the way home with only a forty-five minute connection to the final leg of your journey. Whatever happened to nonstop flights? You were scheduled to arrive in DFW from ATL at 6:39 PM CST and depart at 7:24 PM CST. When you saw the itinerary your travel agent had faxed to you, you remembered the old bromide that declared you couldn't even get to heaven or hell from El Paso without going through DFW. To add insult to injury, the only airfare available to you on such short notice was over $1,500. Your boss wasn't going to like the travel-budget hit, but what could you do? He was the one who had come up with the short-notice travel requirement.

Last night over dinner, you told your spouse that you were estimating that it was a fifty-fifty chance that you'd make the connection in DFW. From prior experience, you knew that a short connection in DFW at that time of day usually was almost impossible to make. Fortunately, there was another flight home from Dallas that was scheduled to leave at 10:27 PM CST. If you missed your connection, you could probably get on that flight if a seat was available. It would mean dinner in the terminal snack shop rather than at home with the family. You decided to put a change of clothes in your overnight bag just in case.

You got up at 3 AM so that you would have enough time to make it to the airport at least an hour-and-thirty minutes before scheduled departure—just in case you were delayed at the security check point. And you needed enough time to eat something because you knew there would be no food on the airline flights. Your connections would be tight and you wouldn't have enough time to eat lunch in Atlanta. Peanuts, pretzels and airline coffee can only carry you so far.

The oh-dark-hundred get-up was tough. Your normal biological rhythm and schedule routinely got you up at 7 AM and to the office by 8:30 AM. Feeling exceedingly groggy, you fumbled through your morning ablutions and watched The Weather Channel while you munched on a bagel and drank your morning coffee. You ate alone because your spouse and children were sleeping, still three hours from the start of their day. You were disappointed that you would have to leave home without saying good morning to them—not your usual custom.

To your great dismay, the weather guessers were predicting clouds, thunderstorms and strong winds throughout the day in

Dallas and Atlanta. To make matters worse, the same weather was forecast for this evening in El Paso—a consequence of the monsoon season currently delivering most of the annual liquid-sunshine allowance for your desert paradise. As an experienced road warrior, you knew that the portents this day did not bode well for a smooth trip through the U.S. air-transportation system.

After briefly considering aborting the trip, you decided to leave for the airport because you knew that your boss wouldn't accept "a little bad weather" as a valid reason to not make the meeting with the client in Atlanta. Maybe you would get lucky and the flight to DFW this morning would be canceled because of the weather there.

As you got up from the table, you inadvertently spilled the bottom half of your last cup of coffee all over your business clothes. It took a few seconds for your sleep-deprived, off-biorhythm mind to realize what had happened. As the hot coffee seeped through the fabric, your sluggish nervous system finally set off alarms. Your blood pressure suddenly increased, the adrenalin kicked in and you simultaneously became very frustrated and angry. It didn't help that these indignities were being heaped upon you at a time that you would normally be sound asleep, enjoying your reliably pleasant dreams. You became even angrier when you realized that the departure time from home that you had carefully selected to allow for an unhurried drive to the airport would now be closer to a panic-stricken stampede out the door by the time you found and changed into fresh attire.

Finally managing to leave home only twenty-minutes later than you had planned, you calculated that if everything went just right on the drive to the airport, you would still have a decent margin for a delay at the security check point. You had planned ahead. No checked bags today, only your briefcase and one small carry-on bag. As you hurried to your car, you enjoyed a secure feeling, knowing full well that you had no logical reason to feel that way.

Unfortunately, everything wasn't going to go smoothly. As you reached down to turn on your headlights, you noticed that the gas tank was almost empty. You'd have to stop for gas on the way to the airport. The fuel stop, along with the two construction zones that must have popped up out of the pavement overnight like evil mushrooms, combined to make your mad dash to the airport equally frustrating and delaying. Waiting forever for a traffic light to let you go, you reflected upon your earlier feeling of security. Could it have possibly been false security?

As you entered the airport parking lot, you glanced up at the still-dark sky to see the brighter stars through sporadic holes in the high, thin clouds. You knew that the cirrus clouds were precursors to the weather that would be moving into the area later in the day. That is, if you remembered your high-school Earth Science course at all.

You parked your car as close to the terminal as possible in anticipation of the thunderstorms that were probably going to greet you when you returned tonight. Due to the new security measures, the closest available parking space was a good half-mile from the terminal. Grabbing your collapsible umbrella, you walked briskly across the lot focusing on getting through the security checkpoint with enough time to make your flight. It was going to be tight.

Since you had been in and out of the El Paso International Airport (ELP) terminal hundreds of times in the course of your many years of air-travel adventures, you knew the shortest route to the security checkpoint at your airline's concourse. This morning, though, your knowledge of the local terrain wasn't going to help much. The backup at the X-ray and magnetometer machines appeared to stretch all the way to DFW. You didn't know there were this many people living in the El Paso area. Where had all these people come from? Where were they going at this ungodly hour of the day? There was no way that you were going to make your flight. You almost turned around and went home, but you decided to give it the old college try. At least you'd have the right story to tell your boss. You were certainly going to give it your best shot.

Standing in line at the security checkpoint, your frustration level was still increasing. Why did everyone take so long to move through the magnetometer? Why was the security guard a somnambulist? Didn't anybody care that you were about to miss your flight? Why was the guard opening your umbrella? Did she think it was a disguised weapon? Could she get it closed again? Could she possibly take any longer to pass you through security?

Finally, after being approved for shipment by Big Brother, you emerged from the confusion of the security checkpoint in a state of mind that bordered on panic. As you dodged around the groups of people and individuals clogging the concourse hallway, you marveled at their ability to be oblivious to their status as impediments to progress. As it turned out, your departure gate was at the very end of the concourse. Your hopes plummeted. The sense of security you had been enjoying earlier completely evaporated.

Breathlessly approaching your departure gate, you noticed that there were at least ten people waiting to check in with the gate agent. Since you had decided to bypass the ticket counter to save time this morning, you had no choice but to check in with the gate agent. How in the world was she going to check in all these people in the five minutes remaining until the scheduled departure time? You knew from experience this airline *always* made sure this flight left on time. It was part of the bank of airplanes that made the first flight of the day into the hub from satellite airports before shuttling around the system all day. If this flight was late, it would have a ripple effect throughout the airline's route network for many hours to come. You just knew they were going to leave without you. They'd done it to you before.

The travel gods smiled upon you, however, and you were the last passenger through the door to the Jetway. You scrambled over the threshold at the last possible second. Issuing a sigh of relief, you plunked yourself down in your assigned seat. Maybe things would go smoothly now that you were safely ensconced in the big silver bird. One can always hope. Snuggling into the too-familiar surroundings of the coach section, the warm feeling of security ebbed back into your soul.

The flight to Dallas was delayed due to low ceilings, rain and high winds at DFW. You arrived at the gate twenty-minutes late, leaving only twenty-five minutes to make your connection. It took almost ten minutes for the Jetway to make its way up to the airplane. By the time the flight attendant opened the heavy cabin door, the passengers were near mutiny.

With little more than fifteen minutes left until your next flight departed, you finally made it into the terminal. A quick check of the monitor screens and you were on your way. It was barely possible that you would be able to change concourses and navigate your way to the far-flung departure gate by scheduled departure time. How could your outbound flight be on time when it appeared that every airplane landing at DFW this morning was running at least twenty-minutes late? Was it an aeronautical mystery? Another last-minute lunge through the door to the Jetway and you had made it! Wonder of wonders, you were going to make it to Atlanta on time—you thought.

The nasty weather at DFW was being augmented this morning, for your traveling pleasure, by a line of thunderstorms lying on a gracefully bowed northeast-southwest line almost exactly halfway between DFW and ATL. Shortly after your aircraft was pushed back from the gate, the captain dolefully informed everyone onboard that they would be arriving in ATL almost one-hour late today due to the weather—if further delays were not incurred. Great! That would leave only three hours for the mad dash downtown, the meeting with the Very Important Client and the mad dash back to ATL for the return flight home. It didn't matter though. You were on your way to Atlanta. No turning back now.

The captain's prognostication had been accurate. You stepped off the airplane in ATL just over one-hour late. After a hurried phone call to your client's office informing them that you were running behind schedule, you jumped into a cab for the thrill ride into the city. Why couldn't cabbies in modern-day America speak English? Why did cabs have to be so rundown and shabby? How many more times would the cabby get lost trying to find your destination? Why hadn't you just crawled back under the covers this morning?

When you identified yourself to your client's receptionist, her face took on that I-don't-want-to-deal-with-this look and she told you to make yourself comfortable while she called your client's assistant. The assistant arrived and informed you that while you were on your way in from the airport, your client had been called away for an important meeting by his boss, and she didn't know when he would be available. After several minutes on a telephone graciously provided by your host, you had finally located your boss and informed him of the situation. It didn't surprise you too much when he told you to scrub the mission and get back home. Your attendance at the 8 AM staff meeting tomorrow morning was critical.

The trip back to the airport was even more annoying than the trip in. An unidentifiable smell in the cab was overwhelming. By the time you reached ATL, your stomach was doing aerobatics and your eyes were watering. However, you were able to overcome your nausea because you knew it would all be over soon. You were on your way home. All you had to do now was sit back, relax and enjoy your ride on a jet plane. Right—what planet did you think you were living on anyway?

As you paid the cabby in front of the ATL departure terminal, you glanced out to the west where several flashes of lightning had caught your eye. In the darkening sky, you could make out a line of towering cumulus clouds marching inexorably towards the airport from the western ramparts of the metropolis. This was undoubtedly the line of thunderstorms that you had flown around earlier on your way into Atlanta. Yes sir, it was certainly going to be a hot time in "Hotlanta" tonight.

Chapter 2: "The Connection"

*"The airplane has unveiled for us
the true face of the earth."*

Antoine de Saint-Exupéry
"Wind, Sand and Stars"

By now, you had only thirty minutes until your flight was scheduled to leave for Dallas. As you approached the security checkpoint, you recalled that last week this terminal had been evacuated because a security guard had inadvertently unplugged an X-ray machine. It had taken over three hours to straighten things out and get the flights moving again. You said a silent prayer that things would go more smoothly this evening. Despite all the challenges you had encountered so far today, your sense of security rose now that you were back in the bosom of the greatest mass-transportation system ever created by man.

Your passage through the security checkpoint was anything but smooth. The lineup for the magnetometer was at least fifty-people deep. It took almost fifteen minutes to reach the front of the line. This was due to the unpleasant fact that the screener was making every third person go through the magnetometer twice. Placing your briefcase and carry-on bag on the belt that would pass them through the X-ray machine (and out of your sight if you didn't hurry through the magnetometer), you quickly sidestepped in front of an old man and lunged through the cattle shoot. Beep, beep, beep, beep...

Oh no! You had just violated the most important rule in the now-current air-traveler's code of conduct—you had set off the alarm. How could this be? Why hadn't you set off the alarm in El Paso this morning? Was the sensitivity on this magnetometer set differently from the one at ELP? Everybody around you stopped and stared, annoyance at your dim-wittedness clearly displayed on their faces. The security guard looked at you with a suspicious eye. You knew you were in for it now.

Calling you back through the magnetometer while everyone outside the security checkpoint was obviously enjoying the spectacle of your discomfiture—after all, you were the best show in town at that moment—the security guard ordered you to turn your pockets inside-out and to remove your belt and shoes. Rebellion, mutiny, mortification—all ran through your mind. However, you had been taught as a child to respect authority. Anyway, what good would it do to argue? They'd probably throw you in the slammer if you did. In the spirit of supporting national security, but with a strong feeling of humiliation, you dutifully complied.

You took off your shoes, emptied your pockets and turned them inside out. As you were removing your belt, you noticed that the guard was putting a rubber glove on her right hand. "What the devil is that for?" you wondered. It didn't take long to find out. The guard stepped behind you and slipped her gloved hand down inside the waistband of your pants. She ran her hand all around your waist and then stuffed your pockets back into your pants. Finished with the body search, she told you to step back through the magnetometer. "Oh well," you thought, "it could have been worse."

After completing your impromptu strip tease for the jaded audience of fellow air travelers, you stepped back through the magnetometer wondering what awful substances might be greedily adhering to the bottom of your socks. This time the sirens and flashing lights didn't go off.

Now bored with you, the security guard pointedly suggested that you get dressed and clear the area so that the more-law-abiding citizens could get to their flights. You wondered what had set the alarms off, which caused you to remember the news report that you had heard only yesterday. The report had noted that a recent undercover security inspection at several major airports, that were now staffed by federal security guards, had revealed the fact that thirty-percent of the guns used in the tests were slipping through the security checkpoints; and that knives were getting through undetected seventy-percent of the time. What kind of security is that? Was all this brouhaha over heightened security resulting in real security, or was it just another case of false security?

Fortunately, your bags were still waiting for you at the end of the X-ray machine's roller chute. You marveled at your luck. You had completely forgotten about them while you were being detained by the Transportation Security Agency's version of homeland security. What are the chances that some airport thief would miss such a ripe opportunity? At least something had to go right on this airline trip from Hell. You chose to be secure in the thought that if you just made the flight to DFW, you'd be home tonight safe-and-sound with your family.

With barely fifteen minutes left until your scheduled departure time, you launched yourself away from the security checkpoint towards the nearest airline monitor screen. After only a few seconds of searching, you found your departure gate listed next to your destination city. You were pleased that your flight would be departing from a nearby gate, but the posted departure time was anything but pleasure-providing. Your flight was now scheduled to depart ATL at 6:30 PM EST—almost one-hour late. How were you going to make your connection in DFW when your planned layover time there was only forty-five minutes?

Your first reaction was to consult a gate agent for clarification of your situation. Unfortunately, every airline representative within sight had at least fifty disgruntled and highly agitated passengers crowded around them. That wasn't going to work. Your next thought was to call the airline's reservations center. After rifling through your briefcase for the itinerary sheet with reservation's phone number on it, you placed the call with your cell phone. A busy signal greeted you the first five times you tried to get through. On the sixth try, you finally connected—with a recording. You were condescendingly informed by the electronic greeting that no real, live agents were available, but please feel free to select from the following menu. There was going to be no real help from the airline's reservations center.

Giving up in frustration, you earnestly wished there was someone you could call to help you out of this mess. Maybe your travel agent could help. Again, it took several tries before you finally reached someone at your travel-agent's office in El Paso. After explaining your situation, the friendly travel agent back home told you she would try to find another way for you to get home tonight. The tone of her voice told you not to put too much hope into an acceptable outcome on that front. She'd call you back.

Another look at the monitor told you the estimated departure time for your flight had just slipped another fifteen minutes. Your level of agitation was increasing faster than the airline delays were mounting. You suddenly had a feeling of foreboding. You really wanted to sleep in your own bed tonight and have breakfast with your family in the morning, not to mention the fact that you just had to be at the staff meeting tomorrow.

However, there was nothing you could do about the situation. Once again, you were caught in the web of weather-induced airline gridlock. You were just another one of the sheep being herded around by disgruntled airline employees. After several deep breaths and a few moments of reflection, you decided to release the problem and take whatever came next. As a veteran air traveler, you knew that was the best thing to do.

You pulled out your cell phone again and called your spouse to announce your delay and break the news that you definitely would not be home for dinner. In fact, you might not be home tonight at all. Your spouse suggested that you consider staying in Atlanta instead of enduring the zoo at the airport. Again, the sense of apprehension welled up like a geyser about to erupt. You had had these premonitions when flying the airlines in the past and they always had turned out to be false alarms. You invariably arrived at your destination alive and kicking—eventually. Pushing your misgivings back down into the well of your subconscious, you allowed your boss's order to be at the staff meeting in the morning to override your feelings. You told your spouse that you had to make it home tonight.

You ambled to your assigned departure gate to wait for whatever the U.S. air-transportation system was going to throw at you next. Bedlam reigned at the departure gate. There was a throng of at least thirty people crowding around the agent-less podium. What did they think they were going to accomplish? Every seat within sight was taken. People were standing everywhere. The pay phones had lines four-people deep waiting for an open phone. Those not waiting for a pay phone were busily talking on their cell phones. You found an unoccupied piece of real estate, put your bags down and prepared yourself to stand for however long it was going to take to get out of town. At least it was a target-rich environment for people watching.

Your cell phone rang. It was your travel agent. She informed you that due to the bad weather in Atlanta and Dallas, your airline's evening schedule was in disarray. Nothing was on time. The same was true of all the other airlines that might have provided you with an alternative way to get home. She suggested that your best bet was to stay with the original plan and fly to Dallas. Since so many flights were running late, you still had a good chance of making some kind of connection in DFW to a flight that would get you home tonight. You thanked her for her "help" and disconnected. This was definitely going to be one of those airline trips to remember.

As you put your cell phone back into your pocket, you noticed that an airplane was pulling into the departure gate. Things were looking up. However, over the aircraft's tail you could see flashes of lightning. They seemed to be moving closer to ATL. You looked at your watch. It was now only fifteen minutes until the re-estimated departure time. You knew from your experience that there was no way the airline could turn the airplane in that time. The departure time was going to slip again. Oh well, you thought, time to spare, go by air. More time yet, go by jet.

Forty-five minutes later, the airplane you were on was finally pushed back from the gate in ATL. It was just after 7 PM EST—almost ninety-minutes late. Your hopes for getting home tonight now rested on the delay of your originally scheduled flight out of DFW or the 10:27 PM CST backup flight. Of course, you did not have a reservation on the later flight. You would just have to trust in your luck.

On this leg of your journey, you had been assigned a window seat. You always preferred a window seat. Fascinated by the miracle of flight, you enjoyed looking out the window. Tonight however, you were not sure that having a window seat was an advantage. You were compelled to look out the window as the airplane moved slowly away from the terminal. You could see the lighting very close to the western boundary of the field and what appeared to be a galaxy of flashing aircraft anti-collision lights suspended above the taxiway. Peering around the window frame at the line of aircraft ahead of yours, you decided there must be a hundred aircraft waiting to takeoff. How long was this going to take?

The captain must have been reading your mind. He came on the passenger-address system with a lazy drawl that immediately told you he must be a good old boy from your home state of Texas. Either that or he had received high marks in the Chuck Yeager School of Pilotspeak. He informed you that you were number twenty-three for takeoff on Runway 26 Left. That was the good news. The bad news was that all departures from ATL had been suspended until the thunderstorms moving across the airport cleared out. His best estimate of your takeoff time was forty-five minutes hence.

That would put you into DFW at approximately 9 PM CST— if there were no further delays. There was still a chance you could make your scheduled connecting flight if it was also running late. However, the backup flight was looking like your best bet. It was scheduled to leave at 10:27 PM CST. You would certainly have enough time to make that flight even if it was running on time. That was not very likely. Would there be seats available or would it be oversold? There was no way to find out now. The airline you were on had recently removed its onboard phones and of course you were prohibited from using your cell phone.

As you sat in your cramped seat listening to the steady drum roll of rain striking the top of the fuselage, you wondered why the airline had decided to move your airplane away from the relative security and freedom of the terminal. It probably had something to do with preserving your takeoff slot. At least that was the usual explanation. You speculated why someone couldn't come up with a better way to run a railroad.

Turning your attention away from the pyrotechnic display going on outside your window, you marveled at how many people were crammed into this narrow aluminum tube. The air was getting stale. The captain must have shut an engine down to conserve fuel during your takeoff delay and the air conditioning system must not be operating optimally. Something to do with air recirculation you supposed. You wondered about the myriad of germs that must be floating around you. How many people with some exotic, foreign disease were happily sharing the air with you this very minute? You had no way of knowing.

Almost one-hour later, the captain came back on the passenger-address system to inform you that the thunderstorms were now east of the airport and that departures had resumed. For the next thirty minutes, you tried to relax as your airplane participated in the airline version of bumper-to-bumper traffic, creeping ever so slowly towards the takeoff position.

An announcement ordering the flight attendants to prepare for takeoff alerted you to your imminent departure from ATL. As the captain advanced the power levers to initiate your takeoff run, you checked your watch. You would be getting off the ground in Atlanta at approximately 9:15 PM EST. That would put you into DFW around 10:15 PM CST. You now started praying that your backup flight was running late.

The flight from ATL to DFW was uneventful—a welcome change. The bad weather had moved out of the DFW area and your flight was cleared to land on Runway 35 Left without any further delay. It was even a relatively short taxi into the terminal and, wonder of wonders, a gate was open for your flight. Things were looking up—you hoped.

Chapter 3: "Hidden Risks"

"A pilot's business is with the wind, with the stars,
with night, with sand, with the sea. He strives to
outwit the forces of nature. He stares with expectancy
for the coming of dawn the way a gardener awaits the
coming of spring. He looks forward to port as to
a promised land and truth for him is what lives in the stars."

Antoine de Saint-Exupéry
"Wind, Sand and Stars"

You emerged from the "people eater" in DFW at 10:22 PM CST. It was time to check the monitor screens for your options, but first you had to push your way through the throngs of other passengers trying to get in and out of DFW. Your scheduled connecting flight was nowhere to be found in the listings on the screens.

The only flight to El Paso tonight was your backup flight, now scheduled to leave at 11:30 PM CST. Noting the departure gate, you headed for it with enroute stops in the restroom and the snack shop for one of those ten-dollar sandwiches. The stop for provisioning was mandatory—your hearty breakfast was wearing thin. The two packages of pretzels the flight attendant had grudgingly thrown at you had done little to assuage your hunger. Completing these absolutely essential tasks, you proceeded to the departure gate.

Bedlam prevailed throughout the terminal. People were everywhere. Some looked like they were settling in for the night. Not a good sign. Reaching your departure gate, you estimated that at least two-hundred people were milling around the departure lounge. If they were all waiting for the last flight to El Paso, there was going to be a problem cramming them all into a one-hundred-thirty-seat airplane. Of course, there was no gate agent at the podium. All you could do was find a place to stand and call your spouse with an update on your aerial odyssey.

Your spouse suggested that you call the airline's reservations center to make a reservation on the flight you were waiting for. Why hadn't you thought of that? From the looks of things in the departure lounge, the flight was oversold. Sure enough, the reservations agent who picked up your call after only three attempts to get through informed you that the flight was indeed oversold. He cheerily offered to put you on the standby list. You despondently accepted his offer.

Around 11 PM, an airline representative finally appeared at the podium. She studiously avoided looking at the line of passengers queuing before her as she merrily pecked away at her computer keyboard. The procession stretched out into the hallway and back toward the security checkpoint for at least two-hundred feet. She eventually announced that all passengers with a reserved seat on the flight would have to check-in with her. A collective moan arose from the crowd. Her pronouncement was definitely not popular.

The biomass reformed itself, the passengers with reserved seats gradually forming a new line and everyone else crowding around the podium. Over thirty-minutes later, the passenger agent had finally confirmed that all the people with reserved seats were on hand. While this was going on, a new-new departure time was posted—midnight. This was not a surprise since there was still no airplane at the departure gate.

The next announcement was no revelation either. The agent told everyone that the flight was oversold and that she was interested in conversing with "volunteers" who would agree to give up their seats on the flight in exchange for a voucher for a hotel room and a reserved seat on the next morning's flight to El Paso. Fifteen minutes later, several people had made their way to the podium and subsequently walked away with a relieved look on their faces. They were obviously heading for a hotel room and a much-needed libation.

A few minutes later, the agent announced that the flight was still oversold. She upped the ante with a coupon for a free flight anywhere on the airline's domestic route system in addition to the hotel voucher and a complimentary seat on the morning flight. This proffer really shook the bushes. The more-savvy air travelers in the throng had been waiting for just this chance. The podium was once again mobbed with "volunteers". You briefly wondered when it was that the U.S. airline system became more like let's-make-a-deal than a reliable and convenient means of transportation.

After the happy volunteers marched off down the hallway, the gate agent announced that she would now check in everyone standing by for the flight. You were dismayed by the number of people who crowded the podium. It took several minutes for the agent to complete the check-in. You invoked the powers of the air-travel gods to keep a seat open for you.

At 11:48, an MD-80 pulled into the gate. A few minutes later, what appeared to be a full boat of passengers erupted from the Jetway and scurried down the hallway towards the baggage-claim area. You envied those who had finally arrived at their destination for the night. Before you could begin the last leg of your journey, you had to be fortunate enough to have your name picked from the standby list for a seat on the flight to El Paso.

It was 12:15 AM CST when the agent finally announced that everyone with a confirmed seat on the flight could start boarding the aircraft. She then spoke the words you had been waiting for—she would now start clearing the standby list. Even though you were exhausted, you perked up in the hope that your name would be called. You had no way of knowing how many seats had been made available by the paid-off passengers.

As you were praying that your name would make it to the top of the standby list before they ran out of seats, you saw the captain and first officer for your flight make their way through the horde at the Jetway. They both looked very tired. It briefly passed through your mind that they appeared to be much too tired to be guiding a 150,000-pound jet through the night sky. You wondered how long they had been on duty. With the airlines' policy of nondisclosure of pertinent safety-related facts—like how long your crew had been on duty—you had no way to find out.

You also marveled at the youthful look of the first officer. She appeared to be no more than eighteen, although you thought she had to be older than that to fly for a major airline. How much flying experience could she have at such a young age? The captain appeared to be in his late thirties. No gray hair. Was he experienced enough to have responsibility for the safety of all these people? Was he mature enough to make very conservative decisions regarding the well-being of your flight and its passengers? As it turned out, there were a few other questions about the pilots that you should have been asking.

Their weary look was the result of a very high level of fatigue. They had been on duty for almost fourteen hours and would have to make it to El Paso within the next two hours to stay within their duty-time limits. If you had known how long they had been on duty, you probably would have headed for a hotel—that is if there were any rooms left within a light year of DFW.

The weariness induced by your grueling travel day had left you in no shape to think clearly, let alone to competently handle heavy machinery and make exacting, life-and-death decisions. The day this crew had endured must have been far more fatiguing than yours. After all, they had to fly the airplanes, not just sit back and relax in the cabin.

Surely, the airline and the FAA wouldn't allow someone as fatigued as these pilots appeared to be to fly tonight. Wouldn't they have insisted that the crew take some rest? You had been hearing for several years that pilot and air-safety groups had been complaining about pilot fatigue and the excessive duty times allowed by the Federal Aviation Regulations. Certainly this problem had been solved by now.

It had been a dirty little secret for some time that the airlines and the FAA were a little too cozy when it came to the rules that govern duty times, crew rest and fatigue. In fact, the Federal Aviation Regulations allowed your crew to get up at a very early hour despite their personal biorhythms, and to then work a sixteen-hour, stress-filled day. You had known about this travesty of good sense for some time now, but you always put it out of your mind. You were relying on the airlines and the FAA to keep you safe. As it turns out, this was another case of false security.

Numerous government and industry studies had shown that a normal person with typical stress levels who has been awake for seventeen hours is more impaired than is allowed under the FAA's rules governing alcohol consumption. The FAA and the airlines did not take this fact into account, although they were well aware of it, when they repeatedly ignored, and attempted to legally extend, the sixteen-hour duty day. It should be obvious to even the most uninformed passenger that a pilot in his sixteenth hour of duty could easily be in at least his seventeenth hour of wakefulness when he made his last landing of the duty day.

Why was this obviously unsafe practice allowed to continue? Industry insiders knew that it was embraced by the airlines because a shorter duty day would require more pilots to fly the airline's schedule. More pilots would mean higher costs. Airline managements' focus on the bottom line precluded any safety-enhancing expenditure that was not imposed on them by the federal government. Fortunately for the airlines, their trade association and their paid lobbyists were very effective at convincing the bureaucrats and politicians that their bottom lines were more important than improving the level of safety enjoyed by their passengers.

Your cockpit crew had started their duty day in Chicago at 10:45 AM CST, reporting for duty one hour before the scheduled departure time of their first flight of the day. Under FAA and their airline's rules, they could therefore be on duty until 2:45 AM CST the following day. It did not matter how long they had been awake, what their personal biorhythms were or how they actually felt. The rules were the rules and every airline pilot was expected to live by them. In fact, until a recent court decision forced the airlines to comply with the sixteen-hour duty day, the FAA and the airlines had interpreted this rule in a manner that allowed them to extend this very dangerous duty-time limit even further if weather or equipment problems caused scheduling delays.

The crew's 10:45 AM report time required an 8 AM wakeup. They needed the time before reporting for duty to take care of their morning routine, eat breakfast, take a few minutes of exercise and make the mad dash from downtown Chicago to O'Hare. When you first saw them at 12:15 AM CST, they had already been awake for over sixteen hours. They would be well past the seventeenth-hour danger point before you got to El Paso.

The long duty day was only one factor in the crew's fatigue profile. This was the fourth day of a four-day trip and they were supposed to be home with their loved ones by now. However, because of the atrocious weather covering the central part of the country, they had been reassigned to fly a series of trips that was now planned to terminate with a layover in El Paso. The crew scheduler had told them to plan to deadhead home tomorrow morning if things didn't change due to the now-dissonant orchestration known as the system schedule plan. That would make it five days on the road and counting.

Last night was the crew's third night in a row in a hotel room this week, and it did not provide the captain with restful slumber. He had been unable to sleep the previous two nights away from home, and last night was no exception. Due to the now-jumbled flight schedule, the crew had been allowed to take only twelve hours free from duty between the time they arrived in Chicago the evening before and the 10:45 AM report time. If their airline had followed the FAA rules to the letter, the crew could have been given only eight hours off.

They had arrived at the layover hotel around midnight and had gone directly to their rooms. Shortly thereafter, the copilot went to the captain's room for a much-needed, stress-reducing drink. Although their airline had a rule that prohibited the consumption of alcoholic beverages within twelve hours of flying one of their airplanes, FAA regulations allowed the crew to drink up to eight hours before flying. On this particular night, the crew decided to ignore their airline's rule and go with the FAA's more-lenient directive.

The drinks helped to relax them, and before long they were caught up in a far-ranging discussion of their lives and desires. Before they knew it, they had talked most of the early morning hours away and they now had less than four hours before their bedside phones would jangle them awake. It certainly appeared to the copilot that their professional relationship was making a transition to a personal one. The changeover had started, she knew, innocently enough at a work-related meeting.

The copilot had asked for the meeting. At the time, the captain was her "den mother"; the management pilot-supervisor who she normally reported to. She was confronted with a situation that she had not encountered before, and she believed she needed the advice of a more-senior aviator. She was also required by company regulations to disclose the particular nature of this problem to her immediate supervisor.

If the problem had occurred only a few months earlier, she would have turned to her father first for the needed advice. He had been an airline pilot for a competing airline for over twenty years and he surely would have been able to help her. However, he had made that last flight over the horizon when he died from a sudden stroke while fishing on a secluded Canadian lake. Every time she thought of him, she regretted that he had not lived to see her achieve their mutual goal—her employment as an airline pilot for a major carrier.

Her father's chief focus in what turned out to be the last years of his life had been to guide her through the complex maze that leads to an airline's new-hire-pilot class. Expert guidance and mentoring was crucial to success—only one out of every hundred people who start out on the long and difficult path to the big leagues of the flying world actually land one of the coveted positions. Her father had been her mentor.

His obsession was due not only to parental concern for her future, but also to the fact that his airline-piloting career had been cut short. It had not been truncated by the normal things that ground a pilot in the prime of his career—medical problems or the demise of his airline—but by airline politics. Her father had been a leader among the pilots of his airline for over a decade when he was ambushed by the company he had worked for, and been loyal to, for over twenty years. He had worked for the airline for almost his entire professional career. His airline had hired him as a very young man and he was only in his early forties when he ran afoul of the political powers that controlled the airline at that time.

He had been very visibly involved in a bitter labor-management dispute at his airline—on the pilots' side. For the four years following the resolution of the conflict, he had been threatened with employment termination by the airline's management several times. These threats resulted from a tenaciously pursued, medically related, progressive-discipline case against him. It was obvious to all concerned that the case was frivolous because the medical problem was well-documented and acknowledged by the company doctor as legitimate.

The legitimacy of the medical problem did not stop the company from charging him with misuse of sick leave every time he put himself on the sick list because of a flare-up of the intense pain he experienced in his inner ear as a result of the medical condition. In fact, he was required by the Federal Aviation Regulations, and he owed it to his passengers, to ground himself if he was not in top condition to fly. None of this mattered to the company however. They continued to harass him on the issue. No one could miss the fact that their real intent was to force him to quit or, if that failed, fire him.

As the final stages of the disciplinary process unfolded, both sides had hardened their positions. Her father, a man of solid principles, repeatedly informed management that he was not going to yield. He told them that he would continue to do the right thing by grounding himself whenever his physical condition was not conducive to safe flight. If they wanted to fire him, that was OK. He had other business interests that would keep his family afloat during the three-year appeal process that would, he was convinced, result in his re-employment and vindication.

Those who have been on the inside of the traditional labor-management struggle between airline pilots and the managers who run the airlines know that, often times, management will work themselves into a corner from which it is impossible to extricate themselves without resorting to what most would call extreme measures. This was one of those times. Her father and the flight-department managers involved in his case were very vocal about their positions and the fact that if he did not relent, he would be fired. Therefore, the case had become a *cause celebre* for the pilot group and the management group alike.

The problem for the managers was that they had indeed trapped themselves. If they did not fire her father, they would lose face with the pilot group and open the door for more sick-leave use by those pilots who had been too intimidated to make use of it when they should. This would surely cost the airlines millions more in pilot expenses and that would not look good on the managers' records. On the other hand, if they fired him, they knew they would be defeated in the ensuing appeal process because the charges against him where essentially bogus. This would result in the legal requirement to rehire him with full back pay, and the pilot group would be even more encouraged to use sick leave when they needed to.

Her father never found out who in the company had come up with the plan, and he never knew who gave the order to carry it out, but it must have come from very high up in the chain of command. In order to extricate themselves from the mess they had put themselves in, the company's management had decided to do whatever it would take to either rein her father in, or force him to resign.

They launched their plan during the Christmas holiday season by assigning a copilot who had been a strike breaker to fly with him on a three-day trip. Although her father had been a very visible leader during the pilot strike at the airline, he did not harbor the intense animosity that most of the pilots of his line demonstrated towards those misguided pilots who had crossed the picket lines. In fact, he went out of his way to make his cockpit an open and congenial place to work, even for those who had tried to, in his opinion, destroy his profession.

Things went fairly smoothly between them, and on the second layover of the trip, the copilot asked the captain to join him for dinner. Her father had accepted the invitation. The dinner and conversation were unremarkable. When her father told the copilot that he was going up to his room to read, the copilot inveigled him to have an after-dinner drink. Her father reluctantly accepted because he did not want the copilot to feel slighted.

While having a drink at the bar, her father was surprised when they were joined by two women who were, it was hastily explained, local friends of the copilot. After one more drink, her father left the group for his room, noting verbally to the copilot that they were only thirty minutes from the company time limit, based upon their departure time in the morning, for alcoholic-beverage consumption.

The next day of flying went without incident. Following the last flight of the sequence and after their post-flight duties had been completed, her father wished the copilot a merry holiday. As her father made his way through the snow-covered parking lot to his car, his only thoughts were of the week he had off before him and the holiday cheer he would be sharing with his family.

He had not even heard from the company for several days when, on New Years morning, the phone rang at 8 AM. He was a little groggy from the previous evening's celebrations when he answered the phone. He was surprised to hear the voice of the chief pilot of his domicile. Although they had been flying friends and coworkers for years, he did not expect to be hearing from the chief pilot so early on a scheduled day off—and it was a holiday too. What the chief pilot said shocked him into total clarity.

He was, the chief pilot informed him, hereby immediately grounded pending the investigation of charges that he had been drinking on his last layover well beyond the time when he should have stopped imbibing. After recovering from his shock, her father had asked the chief pilot, as an old friend, just what was going on since he was certain that he had not broken any company or FAA rules regarding drinking or anything else. The chief pilot told him not to worry, that he thought this was just a mistake and to report to his office at 8 AM the next morning.

Her father had spent all of New Years day calling his close friends within the airline to try to find out what was happening. Mysteriously, he could not locate the copilot he had flown the trip with. At the end of the day, he was fairly certain of only one thing—either this was a mistake or the company was setting him up for a fall.

He dutifully reported to the chief pilot's office at the appointed hour. Instead of the chief pilot, he found another old pilot friend who was now a management pilot. After cordially greeting her father, the management pilot told him to come along to the airline's medical department. On the way, the management pilot was very reticent and only made small talk.

Waiting for them in a conference room were the airline's chief doctor, the union's employee-assistance-program representative (who was another old pilot friend) and a manager who her father did not know—he was introduced as the company's director of employee assistance. After everyone was seated, the unknown manager opened the meeting.

He informed her father that someone had reported to the company that he had been drinking inside the company's twelve-hour bottle-to-throttle rule. Based on this report, the company was giving him only two choices. He could either leave the conference room and board a flight that was leaving within the hour for the west coast, or he would be fired for breaking the company's drinking rule. When her father asked about the flight's destination, he was told it was Los Angeles. When he asked why there, he was told that Los Angeles was the location of the clinic to which he would be admitted for an evaluation for alcoholism.

Like seeing runway lights appear out of the murky gloom, her father saw clearly now that he was being railroaded by the airline before his sick-leave disciplinary process could reach its climax. Thinking rapidly, he asked the unidentified manager's permission to speak privately with the union representative. The unidentified manager reluctantly agreed to a five-minute break.

Fully expecting the union pilot to be as mystified as he was about this unprecedented procedure for handling suspected pilot-alcoholism issues, her father recalled for both of them what the airline's history had been in such cases. It had always been company practice to confront any pilot suspected of having a drinking problem, ask him if he needed help and then to inform him that if he manifested alcoholism in any way subsequently, he would be investigated and disciplined if necessary. In other words, pilots at this airline had never been confronted with the choice he was being given based solely on one unsubstantiated allegation. In reply, the union pilot agreed with him but told him rather sheepishly that his hands were tied. He strongly recommended that her father get on the airplane for LA.

Now her father was sure that he was being framed. He was positive that he had not broken his airline's drinking rules. He also knew he wasn't an alcoholic. He was convinced that this was the first time that the airline had ever insisted that a pilot be evaluated for alcoholism based on an uninvestigated and unproven first report of illegal drinking, and he now was convinced that the union was in on the frame-up.

It did not surprise him that the union leadership at his airline would not stand up for him. They should have, given his critical service to the pilot group during the strike and this blatant attempt by the company to railroad him so that they could extricate themselves from their dilemma. The union leadership would not defend him because they wanted him out of the way even more desperately than the company.

For the past several months, the union had been promoting a pilot-led buyout of her father's airline. Her father was, in fact, enthusiastically supportive of the concept of the pilots purchasing a controlling interest in the airline. He felt that this strategy would counter many of the negative consequences of airline deregulation that were plaguing all airline-pilot groups at that time. However, he did not agree with the method by which the union proposed to get the job done.

The union was attempting to sell the idea of an Employee Stock Ownership Program, or ESOP, to the pilots. Her father knew that this was not the best way to get control of the company and that ESOPs held inherently dangerous traps for unwary employee groups. He had arrived at these conclusions during the period surrounding the strike when he had chaired a union-approved committee that was charged with designing a pilot buyout of the carrier. This committee had been formed because her father had insisted on it as a condition of his participation as one of the leaders of the striking pilots. Shortly after the strike, the committee had reported to the union leadership on the best way to do the buyout— it was not with an ESOP.

As often happens in any political body, leadership changes and the tides of time work together to drastically alter the course of events. This was one of those times. In the years since the strike, a new, dynamic leader had emerged at the top of the union representing the pilots of her father's airline. This new leader had large appetites. He wanted to be both president of his union and the CEO of his airline. This twin desire biased his thinking about the buyout. The only way he could control the buyout process from his position as a union leader was to use an ESOP. He therefore ignored her father's, and many others' warnings about the dangers of using an ESOP.

This new leader's popularity with the pilot group was immense because of his highly visible role during the strike. Although the new leader enjoyed a warm reception for his ideas regarding the buyout, her father's vocal opposition to the plan was causing him a great deal of concern. As time went by, more and more pilots were moving toward her father's view of how the buyout should be handled.

A crucial vote on the buyout was coming up in the near future. It would benefit the new leader's plans immensely if her father were out of the picture. All that he had to do was sit quietly and let the company do his dirty work for him. The union would only do what was required of it by law. That was to "represent" her father in the process that would lead to his termination and the appeals procedure. The new leader would simply not apply the political pressure that only he could wield. This political force was the only thing that could save her father from being fired.

The extent of the forces arrayed against him, now so obviously revealed, surprised her father. Then, after a moment's consideration, he saw that the strategy made sense—for them. He decided to do his best to outmaneuver his adversaries. His first decision was to not comply with the company's demands that he leave town immediately for some unknown fate.

Returning to the conference room, her father informed the group that he would not be boarding the flight to Los Angeles. The shocked and dismayed faces on the other men revealed that they had not been expecting her father to make this choice. After a rather long period of silence, the mystery manager began to press home his insistence that her father undergo the evaluation "for his own good". Interestingly enough, the other men in the room, including the company doctor who knew him well, were eerily silent.

Her father took control of the meeting by demanding to know who had made the allegation against him. The mystery manager told him that they couldn't reveal that information or any of the details of the charge. Her father asked about the evaluation process they wanted him to go through. The company doctor told him rather shamefacedly that it would be conducted in a clinical setting by a team of psychologists. When asked by her father about the length of the process, the doctor told him that it was open-ended—it could take several weeks or several months.

Like everyone else on the planet who regularly consumed alcoholic beverages, her father was well aware of the many reports that psychologists considered even people who never took a drink to be alcoholic if the psychologists decided that these people harbored certain personality traits. In other words, a person's actual drinking habits had little to do with whether or not the psychologists classified someone as an alcoholic. Her father knew that there was very little chance that company-paid psychologists would not find it in their best interests to hang that label on him. With the almost-certain knowledge that he would be diagnosed to be alcoholic if he went through the company's evaluation program, he explored what would happen after that determination was made.

The mystery manager told him that if he was diagnosed as an alcoholic, he would be required to go through a company- and FAA-approved alcohol-rehabilitation program. This process was also open ended, but it usually, he was informed, took several months.

Following successful completion of the rehab program, he would be required to attend daily support-group meetings for a minimum of two years. When the company and the FAA felt that he was properly rehabilitated, they would have him evaluated once again and they might, at their sole discretion, allow him to return to flying. During this entire time, he would be required to surrender his medical certificate—he would be grounded. If he was allowed to return to flying, he would be required to never take even a sip of an alcoholic beverage for the rest of his flying career. If he did and it was brought to the attention of the airline and the FAA, he would be permanently grounded.

Her father then asked about his employment status during this process. He was told that he would be put on medical leave, but due to the fact that he had used up most of his paid sick leave with the medical problem that he was about to be fired for, he would be on unpaid sick leave for virtually the entire several years the process would take. Her father swore that he could detect the slightest of smiles on the mystery manager's face as he delivered this little piece of news.

Turning to the union representative, her father asked about the appeal process that would follow his termination if he chose to not undergo the company's obviously rigged evaluation for alcoholism and the ensuing equally prejudiced rehab program. The union rep informed him that it would take at least three years to go through all the stages of the appeal process. Of course, he would not be employed by the airline during this time and the FAA would probably pull his medical if the company pressed the issue with them.

Her father could not help but admire the cleverness of the frame-up. If he chose to go through the alcoholism evaluation, there was little doubt in his mind that he would be labeled as an alcoholic. He was also convinced that if he entered the rehab program, it was virtually certain that the company would never agree that he was ready to return to flying. And even if they did, he would spend the rest of his career under management's thumb.

If he chose to fight the allegation, the company would fire him, the FAA would probably take his medical away, and it would be several years before he would even be able to try to prove his innocence of the charges. This choice also carried with it disgrace in addition to the loss of income and quite possibly the loss of his flying privileges forever. Choosing this course also meant that a pending business deal that was critical to him might fall apart if it became known that he had been fired from the airline for alleged alcoholism. He was certain the company would make sure it was widely known why he was no longer with the company.

After only a few moments reflection, her father had looked slowly into each man's eyes in turn and then told them that he was very disappointed in the behavior of the doctor and his fellow pilots. He stated that he knew that they knew that he was not an alcoholic. None of them said or did anything to express denial of this assertion. He then told them that he believed that he was being railroaded because he had the company in a tight spot on the sick-leave issue and because he was causing both the company and the union problems with slipping their ESOP plan by the pilot group. The men who he had known well for years sat mutely with downcast eyes.

It was painfully obvious to her father that only the mysterious manager held any power in this situation, and he was clearly under orders to carry out the company's plan. He asked the manager what would happen if he just got up and walked out of the room. The mysterious manager told him that he would be immediately fired.

Her father thought for a moment, reached into his briefcase and withdrew a note pad. On the top sheet he wrote: I hereby immediately resign my position as a pilot for this airline. He signed it, tore the sheet off and handed it to the mysterious manager. With a rye, resigned look on his face, her father had gotten slowly out of his seat, turned and walked out the door without saying another word. He walked to his car with the certain knowledge that his career as an airline pilot was over. His goal now was to ensure that his daughter made it into the august ranks of airline piloting—at another carrier.

His daughter had turned to her pilot-supervisor for advice on how to handle her problem because her father was no longer around to help her. He had died only a few years after he was railroaded out of his career. The problem she needed to discuss was an investigation the FAA was conducting. It involved a flight she had flown in the airplane her father had given her as a present before he passed away. Although the incident occurred on a personal flight, she was required by her airline's rules to report any situation that involved a possible FAA violation against her.

On this particular flight, which was being conducted for her personal transportation, she made a visual approach to the left runway of what was a pair of parallel runways. The weather was good and she was instructed by approach control to follow an airliner that she could see ahead of her. The wind was blowing across the runways from right-to-left. This was not an unusual situation. It was one she had become very familiar with during her stint as a charter pilot flying light-twin-engine aircraft.

The position she found herself in on the subject flight was widely known in the piloting profession as a very dangerous situation if not handled properly. The source of the danger was a phenomenon known as "wake vortex" or "wake turbulence". Wake vortices are essentially horizontal tornadoes that are formed at the wingtips by the unequal distribution of pressure between the top and bottom of an aircraft's wing. It is one of the more-insidious dragons that lie in wait for unwary aviators. Wake vortices have been known to suddenly reach out and hurl a light airplane into the ground. It usually happens if the pilot of a smaller airplane gets too close to an airliner that is on an approach to the same runway.

Because this had happened many times, and since it continued to happen all too frequently, the aviation industry had spent a lot of time and money making pilots aware of the problem and training them to avoid encounters with the dragon. In this case, she had determined that her best course of action was to fly on the upwind side of the approach course—to the right of the runway— and to use an unusually steep glidepath to a touchdown point beyond the one used by the airliner. This was because the wake vortex that was coming off the airliner's right wingtip was probably drifting downwind—toward the runway's centerline—and sinking below the glidepath used by the airliner. Her chosen approach path should have kept her to the right of, and above, the airliner's wake turbulence.

The procedure she chose conformed to FAA edicts concerning wake turbulence avoidance and it had been taught to her by several of her instructors. In the mind of any experienced pilot, she would be considered to be acting in a prudent manner to avoid the potentially lethal wake vortices. If she had not taken the precautions and then crashed, the FAA surely would have blamed her for acting in a reckless and dangerous manner.

However, there were two factors that came into play that created a situation that would result in the FAA's investigation of her actions on that flight. The first was the fact that the tower controller handling her flight was a trainee. The second was the proximity of the two parallel runways to each other. The runway centerlines were only one-thousand feet apart—very close together for parallel runways.

Her strategy called for her to stay to the right of the left runway's centerline—the runway upon which she intended to land—and to touch down about fifteen-hundred feet down-runway from the threshold. She considered the fact that her final-approach track would put her on, or close to, the extended centerline of the right runway. This did not concern her however because she knew that landings were not being conducted on the right runway—only takeoffs. This was confirmed by the fact that a Boeing 737, which she could easily see, was sitting in takeoff position on the right runway. Her intention was to move over to the left runway's centerline about one mile from its approach end. This would allow her plenty of time to line up for her landing and it would keep her away from the airliner's wake vortices.

As she approached to within approximately two miles of the airport, the tower controller unexpectedly commanded her to "go-around". She complied immediately and followed the controller's instructions to then land on the right runway.

As she taxied the airplane clear of the runway, the ground controller told her to call the tower chief after she parked her airplane. After a little thought, she concluded that the tower controller wanted to apologize to her for what was probably just another air-traffic-control screw up. She proceeded to the ramp and shut the engines down. She went into the fixed base operator's office unconcerned about the request to call the tower chief. After all, she had not, she believed, broken any rules or caused any traffic conflicts.

The tower chief told her that the controller (he did not reveal the fact that he was a trainee) had sent her around because he believed that she was going to land on the right runway instead of the left runway. However, the tower chief made it clear that no traffic-separation standards had been violated due to the incident.

This news was greeted on her part by consternation and more than a little frustration. She believed that she had selected the safest course for her flight, and now the FAA tower chief was saying that he assumed that she had her head up-and-locked. Landing on the wrong runway was one of the more embarrassing and potentially dangerous mistakes that an aviator can make.

As she formulated her reply to the tower chief, she took a deep breath and remembered her father's advice that almost all misunderstandings between pilots and controllers could be resolved with an open, honest exchange of viewpoints. Heeding her father's counsel, she candidly explained what she had been doing. When she finished, the tower chief, without any further comments or questions, told her that he would be reporting the incident to the local FAA Flight Standards District Office for investigation. She was shocked.

A few days later, she received a phone call from the FAA inspector who had been assigned to the investigation. She calmly explained the situation from her perspective and reviewed for the inspector the safety guidelines she had been following. He acknowledged the danger of wake turbulence, but informed her that his mind was already made up—he would be charging her with a violation of the Federal Aviation Regulations.

She was mystified by this turn of events. This must be one of those "badge-and-gun" FAA inspectors that she had been reading about in the aviation press. She knew that she needed some expert advice right away. This is what had prompted her to request the meeting with her supervisor at the airline.

✈

Her supervisor readily agreed to meet with her to discuss the problem. He had been her first and only pilot-supervisor since she had been assigned to line flying after the completion of her initial training program. She had flown with him on a one-day trip to complete her checkout and she noted that he was handsome, very charismatic, highly professional and apparently unavailable. His wedding ring and his comments about the kids he loved gave her the impression that he was "very married". Since she was single and therefore at least casually on the lookout for a suitable partner, she put him in the "not available" category.

When she told him about the incident and the FAA's allegations, he became quite agitated. At first she thought that he was going to fire her, but it turned out that he was indignant about the FAA's attack on her. From the way she described the event, he believed that no professional pilot worth his or her salt would interpret her actions the way the FAA inspector was doing. He was aware of the FAA's recent change in its official attitude towards pilots. It seemed like more and more they were charging pilots with violations of the regulations in cases where only a few years before, it would have been handled in a manner that included a lot of professional respect and give-and-take.

Once again, it looked like the FAA was trying to cover up an error that they had made. It was obvious to her supervisor that it had been a mistake when the trainee told her to go-around. He should have asked her about her intentions before making that decision. This would have easily clarified which runway she intended to land on. The tower chief was undoubtedly covering himself by reporting the incident to the FAA inspector in a way that was most-conducive to his professional survival. He was also ignoring the fact that the pilot-in-command is ultimately responsible for the safety of his or her flight.

The FAA inspector was obviously not willing to listen to reason and it was clear to her supervisor that this was probably due to the inspector's relative lack of experience in aviation. In its efforts to beef up aviation safety, the FAA had been hiring many inspectors who in past years would have been considered too inexperienced to do the job properly.

Her supervisor told her not to worry. He would help her in any way that he could to fight the FAA and keep them from suspending her pilot certificate. Her admiration for the captain expanded exponentially. She felt a great deal of fondness for him now that he had taken a personal interest in her. The affection seemed to flow in both directions. He told her that he would schedule himself to fly with her the following month since he had to put in a month on the line and she needed her periodic line check. This sounded good to her. Who knew? Maybe things weren't going so well in his marriage after all and she could change her opinion of his status from "very married" to "somewhat married".

In fact, things had not been going very well for the captain for some time now. He was in the middle of a very contentious divorce that had been dragging on for over a year with no end in sight. By the time you saw him in DFW preparing to take command of the airplane that would wing you home, he was extremely fatigued and distracted. He was so fatigued and distracted that if he had been given a test for impairment, it would have revealed that he was more impaired than if he were legally drunk.

You also didn't know that this particular captain had a secret even his copilot didn't know about. Three years ago, he had tried to kill himself. The triggering event for this episode was his discovery of his wife's infidelity. Shortly after she had confronted him with this revelation and walked out the door, he had gone into the closed garage, started his car, reclined his seat and drifted off into what he hoped would be relief from his terrible pain. The only thing that saved him was his wife's unexpected return home.

When she opened the garage door with her remote control, the noxious fumes quickly dispersed and he slowly regained consciousness. He had tried to cover up his attempted suicide, but his wife had already figured things out. She called the police, their family doctor and his supervisor at the airline. The airline immediately grounded him and sent him for a psychological evaluation. The doctors had determined that he could be rehabilitated. He entered the airline's employee assistance program and, two years later, he was back flying for the airline again.

Had you known that you were about to entrust your life to a person who was impaired beyond the legal limits of sobriety, who had tried to commit suicide and who was severely distracted by an ugly divorce and the beginnings of an affair, you definitely would have reconsidered the wisdom of engaging with him in the delicate art of aviation. However, you knew none of this. Although you had noticed that the captain looked tired, who would believe that the airline and the FAA would sanction this person to make this flight? Once again, this was clearly a case of false security.

You were also unaware of other factors in the captain's life that mitigated against a safe flight tonight. Although he was flying as a regular line pilot tonight, he knew that the other pilots at his airline, including his young copilot, saw him in a leadership and supervisory role. He had a certain image to live up to. You didn't know it, but his response to these factors would have a significant impact on your safety this evening.

You also did not know that the pilots on this particular airline were several months into a very contentious labor-contract dispute. Many of the line pilots had made safety-related decisions that were heavily biased towards the side of safety. Some of these situations had revolved around duty time, fatigue and a pilot's legally imposed responsibility to self-police his ability to safely make a flight. Many of these decisions had negatively impacted the airline's ability to maintain their published schedule. This situation was further exacerbated by the fact that the airline was short of pilots.

Management had made the decision two years ago to reduce pilot hiring in the hope that they could gain concessions from the current pilot group that would allow the hiring of new pilots at a lower pay rate than the existing pilots. The word had been surreptitiously spread throughout the pilot-management team that when flying the line, they should demonstrate the "proper leadership" when it came to decisions regarding duty time and fatigue.

As it turned out, your captain's desire to conform to the dictates of his management peers caused him to decide to fly to El Paso tonight despite the fact that he was really not at his best. He knew that he and his copilot would be pushing their duty-time limits, and frequent industry reports had alerted him to the fact that this combination could prove fatal. The desire to be accepted by his superiors and peers had been inculcated in him while an undergraduate at the Air Force Academy. He adhered to this creed throughout his military career and he intended to continue this policy with his current outfit. An important link in the chain of errors that lead to a tragedy was put in place with the captain's decision to demonstrate the "proper leadership" in this situation.

The copilot, although not suffering from a level of fatigue as acute as the captain's, was nonetheless suffering from other impairment-inducing factors. With just six months under her belt at the airline, she was extremely eager to demonstrate her willingness to conform to the group norms and to perform at a highly professional level. These desires could easily cause her to not question the captain's decisions as a more-experienced copilot would certainly do.

Over the course of flying together this month, the captain and first officer had spent many, many hours together in the stress-filled environment of a modern jet cockpit. During this time, she had frequently admired the superb airmanship and self-confidence displayed by the captain. Over several meals together, he had regaled her with his aerial exploits as a fighter pilot in the Gulf War. She might not have been as fatigued as the captain, but she was afflicted with a severe case of hero worship.

The fact that he was going through a divorce and she was single only drew her closer to him. She had started to harbor feelings of intimacy towards him and she was careful to favorably impress him at every opportunity. This fostered in her a desire not to challenge her captain. This reluctance to assert herself added another link to the error chain.

Another factor working against the safety of the flight this evening was the fact that the copilot had been under a lot of pressure from the company to fly despite the fact that she had a recurring medical problem. It was a condition that caused her great pain in her right ear after only a few hours of high-stress flying. She had inherited the problem from her father. There was no cure. She could find relief only by taking several days off from flying. The airline's own doctors had confirmed the diagnosis made by the specialist, but management insisted that she not use her sick leave so often.

Since she was still on probation and the airline could fire her without cause, she would often choose to fly rather than abide by the FAA regulation prohibiting her from flying with any medical problem that might impair her ability to fly safely. Her problem was acting up again tonight, but there was no way that she was going to put herself on sick leave.

Deep in your reverie over the cockpit crew, you almost missed your name when it was called by the gate agent. Hurrying to the podium, you were handed a boarding pass and told to hurry onto the airplane. The Jetway door would be closing shortly. In the rush to make the flight home, you pushed your misgivings about the captain and first officer down into your subconscious and quickly boarded your jet.

As you stepped over the threshold of the forward entry door, you glanced over your left shoulder into the cockpit. You could see the captain and first officer studiously going through their pre-departure cockpit checks. Everything looked normal. Why had you been concerned? You made a right turn and proceeded down the aisle toward your assigned seat—33D.

Passage down the aisle was not easy. Several passengers who had boarded ahead of you were still standing in the aisle, fussing with coats and trying to stuff oversized bags in the overhead bins. The flight was full—a smiling face in every window and a happy butt in every seat. You were just thankful to be making it home tonight.

Finally reaching the row where your seat was located, you discovered that you were going to have to crawl over a large man sitting in the aisle seat. He obviously wasn't going to get out of his seat to make it easy for you to get to your center seat. Oh well, you thought, I can endure one more indignity. I'll be home soon. As you lowered yourself into the seat, you noticed that the window seat next to you was occupied by a young boy who appeared to be about the same age as your oldest son. You knew how your son would act if tired, confined to a small space and surrounded by strange people. You hoped this young man would comport himself in a much better manner.

You had just buckled your seatbelt when you felt the airplane moving back from the gate. The engines were started as you got your paperback book out of your briefcase and settled in for the two-hour flight home. It had been a very long day, but it would be over soon. Maybe a drink or two on the flight home would make things a little more tolerable. At least you would have an interesting story to tell at the staff meeting in the morning. It would definitely top all the other recent airline-horror stories that were certain to be shared before the meeting got underway.

It seemed like it was only a few minutes later when the captain came on the passenger address system to inform you that you were now only ten-minutes from landing in El Paso. Those two drinks had certainly helped to make the flight go more quickly.

The captain said that he was planning to land on Runway 26 Right because of strong winds out of the west-northwest on the surface and the fact that Runway 26 Left—which was 9,025 feet long—was closed due to construction. Runway 26 Left was the runway the captain would prefer to land on because the wind is from the west-northwest at thirty knots with gusts to forty-five knots.

The longest runway on the airport, 12,010-foot-long Runway 4/22, was out of the question because the strong northwesterly winds would exceed the crosswind limits of the MD-80 if he tried to land on it. He is locked into using Runway 26 Right. As an afterthought, the captain cautioned everyone about the likelihood of "some bumps" close to the ground because of the high winds.

Leaning over the boy in the window seat, you take a quick look out the window. You can see lights on the ground. That's good, but you can also see flashes of lightning off to the right of the airplane. You briefly wonder about the weather for your landing, but you are once again lulled into a sense of well-being by telling yourself that the flight crew certainly must know what they are doing. As it turns out, this is definitely another case of false security.

Things are not going very well in the cockpit. The captain is by now very tired. It is almost 1:30 in the morning MST, 2:30 AM CST, and he only has a few minutes left until he and the copilot break through their sixteen-hour duty-time limit. He is not thinking very clearly and things are deteriorating rapidly at the El Paso International Airport. There are thunderstorms south, west and north of the airport. Thankfully, the course inbound to the airport is clear of "thunder-boomers".

The problem with Runway 26 Right is that it is only 5,493-feet long and half as wide as the other runways. At the aircraft's estimated landing weight this morning, the runway is just long enough, but in this wind, the captain will certainly have to use a large share of his flying skills to make a safe landing on this narrow, relatively short strip of concrete.

Another problem with Runway 26 Right that the captain is aware of, but you aren't, is that this runway can be used in visual-flight-rules conditions only. It has no electronic-navigational aids that will help him to line the airplane up with the runway and to maintain the proper glide slope on his approach to a landing. This would have been challenging enough in daylight with reasonable winds, but at night with a strong crosswind and very few visible ground lights, the task is much more difficult and risky.

Had the captain been less fatigued and if he had more time to make a well-reasoned decision, he might have elected not to land in El Paso. However, his options were few. The alternate for this flight is Tucson International Airport, 233 nautical miles and fifty-minutes to the west. The problems with going to the alternate are manifold.

First, the captain can see a line of thunderstorms out to the west of El Paso on the MD-80's airborne-weather radar. Unfortunately, due to the relatively low altitude the airplane is now at, he can't tell how far to the north the line extends. He doesn't know how far he would have to fly to get around the line and fuel is getting critical. A deviation to the south is not an option due to the restrictions imposed by the U.S.-Mexico border and the thunderstorms he can see in that direction.

Even if he could get to Tucson before the fuel runs out, he knows that the airplane and its passengers will be stuck there until sometime later that morning. He and his copilot would not be able to fly again until they've had a legal rest. As far as he knows, no other crews from his airline are laying over there tonight. A decision to go to Tucson would not only greatly inconvenience the passengers, but it would also cost his airline untold thousands of dollars.

His other option is to turn around and go back to DFW. He has enough fuel to make it—just—if he makes the decision to divert right now. He knows that although there will probably be a crew in DFW who can fly the airplane in the morning, the airline is counting on the airplane being in El Paso tonight so that it can be used on the first flight in the morning back to DFW. If the airplane isn't there when the morning crew and passengers arrive at the airport, a monkey wrench will be thrown into the finely tuned works of the system-schedule plan for most of the day.

The prudent course of action (returning to DFW), the one the captain should choose, is not even considered because of the captain's psychological bias towards completing his assigned mission and his desire to set an example for the line pilots. He wants to show the recalcitrant pilots on the airline's payroll that with a little fortitude and commitment to the company, schedule integrity can be maintained. He has already made the decision to land the airplane on Runway 26 Right at ELP.

Chapter 4: "False Security"

"You'll be bothered from time to time by storms, fog, snow.
When you are, think of those who went through it before you,
and say to yourself, 'What they could do, I can do'."
                                    Antoine de Saint-Exupéry
                                    "Wind, Sand and Stars"

Once the decision to land in El Paso was made, the die was cast. If everything went just right, a safe landing would be forthcoming. If anything went wrong, the outcome would be much less satisfactory.

Your flight is told to switch communications frequencies from the center controller to approach control. The first officer is handling the radio work while the captain flies the airplane. Upon checking in with ELP approach control, she is instructed by the controller to turn right to a heading of 280 degrees and descend to 7,000 feet for radar vectors to the instrument-landing-system (ILS) approach to Runway 22. Immediately after hearing these instructions, the captain banks the airplane towards the newly assigned heading, retards the power levers and pitches the nose down to set up the descent to 7,000 feet.

After a few seconds of confusion, the first officer asks the captain if he is going to land on Runway 22 or 26 Right. This inquiry on the part of the first officer is commendable—it is what she has been trained to do. However, she has not participated in, nor questioned, his decision to use the shorter runway. If she had, the false security you are enjoying back in the cabin might turn out to be real security. Unfortunately, for this flight and everyone aboard, her deference to the captain, her fatigue and her inexperience causes her to miss this vitally important detail.

The captain orders the first officer to tell approach control that they want to land on Runway 26 Right. The first office does as she is told. After a few seconds hesitation, the approach controller "rogers" their intentions and tells them to turn left to a heading of 190 degrees for the radar vector to Runway 26 Right. He also instructs the crew to report the ELP airport in sight. This is going to be a visual approach, so the crew has to have the airport in sight before the controller can clear them for the approach. They will then be on their own.

As the flight descends, the first officer focuses her attention outside the airplane—looking intently for any sign of the airport and Runway 26 Right. The captain meanwhile is manually flying the airplane and consulting the weather-radar display. The thunderstorms south, west and north of the field are closing in. It is very difficult to tell for sure, but the captain decides that his race with the thunderstorms is going to be a dead heat. He pushes the power levers up to high-power in an attempt to beat them. He is anxious to get on the ground and he presses the first officer for a sighting of the airport.

Leaving 7,500 feet, the turbulence begins. It is only a nibble at first, but it quickly escalates to moderate turbulence as the aircraft descends closer to the waiting desert. Anything that is not secured is flying around the cabin. Up front, the dimly lit cockpit displays are difficult to see, let alone interpret. You cinch your seatbelt down another notch, fold your hands in your lap and peer out the cabin window. You can see only an occasional light on the ground due to the sparsely populated desert east of El Paso. Still in the grip of the turbulence, the airplane suddenly rolls steeply to the right. You find yourself looking almost straight down at the Fort Bliss Military Reservation.

Up in the cockpit, the captain has his hands full just controlling the airplane. The turbulence is causing the airplane to roll from side-to-side over thirty-degrees at a time. He is having great difficulty arresting the momentum of the rolling airplane. He struggles to get the wings back to near-level flight. He can barely see his airspeed indicator and altimeter. The needles are a blur and he can only guess at these two very-important pieces of information.

He realizes that he should have anticipated the turbulence. Whenever the wind speed exceeds twenty knots over uneven terrain, moderate-to-severe turbulence can be expected. He had not thought of this factor when he made his decision to land at El Paso because his fatigued state has severely impaired his ability to think clearly. What might have been a minor oversight in another situation could prove to be another link in the chain of errors that can lead to an accident.

With the worsening turbulence, the captain briefly considers abandoning the approach and heading for DFW. However, he quickly moves past this decision point. His attention is now focused on getting the airplane on the ground before the thunderstorms roll over the airport. He can now clearly see cloud-to-ground and cloud-to-cloud lightning arrayed like a monumental fireworks display to the west of the airport. If the captain had not been so distracted by fatigue and his personal problems, he would have recognized the fact the he was entering a danger zone within which a very treacherous dragon was lurking.

The aircraft is rapidly approaching 7,000 feet which is approximately 3,000 feet above the elevation of the airport. The only pertinent electronically provided navigation data the captain has to work with is a read-out on his distance-measuring-equipment (DME) which is providing him with the distance from his airplane to a radio transmitter located near the approach end of Runway 4 at ELP. This distance is direct-line-of-sight, or slant-range.

Due to the placement of the DME transmitter, the configuration of the runways at ELP and the inherent limitations of the equipment, he is able to derive only an approximate distance to the threshold of Runway 26 Right. In addition to all his other tasks and problems at the moment, he has to do some mental math to compute his distance from touchdown. His computations tell him, if they are correct, that the airplane is now only five miles from the end of the runway upon which he intends to alight.

This is a problem. At an altitude of 7,000 feet, the captain figures that the airplane is over 1,500 feet higher than it should be to set up properly for the approach. However, the approach controller cannot clear the flight below 7,000 feet until the crew reports the airport in sight. The captain slows the airplane and calls for incrementally greater flap settings as the airplane decelerates. He again asks the first officer if she can see the airport as he sneaks a peek outside. In the cabin, you can hear the flap motor whine and feel the airplane shudder as the flaps are extended. You have never been in turbulence this severe before. Kicking yourself for pushing aside the foreboding you experienced earlier today, you are now becoming concerned about the outcome of this flight.

The airplane is now approaching four-miles from the runway as the first officer announces to the captain that she has the airport beacon, but not Runway 26 Right, in sight. The captain tells her to report to approach control that they have the airport in sight. After she communicates with the controller, the captain asks the tower to turn the runway lights on 26 Right up to full intensity. The approach controller clears the flight for a visual approach and instructs the flight to contact ELP tower.

The captain immediately retards the power levers to idle, pitches the nose down and starts a right turn that he hopes will put him on the final approach course. He is making this maneuver as much from instinct as from certainty about where the runway is. As he rolls out on the runway heading, the tower controller turns the runway lights full up.

A quick glance out the cockpit window reveals the now-visible runway to the captain. It sure looks short and skinny. He knows his ability to judge his glidepath is impaired by the darkness and the dearth of ground lights on the approach path to the runway. This is truly going to be a dark-hole approach. It is one of aviation's most dangerous procedures, particularly when no electronic guidance to the runway is available. The so-called "non-precision" approach is perfectly legal according to the FAA and sanctioned by most airlines; but that doesn't make it a good idea, especially in a situation like this one.

Calling for gear down, the captain hears the first officer negotiate a landing clearance on Runway 26 Right. The tower controller informs them that the wind is now from 280 degrees at thirty knots with gusts to forty knots. This is not going to be a piece of cake.

The noise made by the landing gear being extended provides a brief respite for your jangled nerves. Even though the turbulence is getting a little worse as you get nearer to terra firma, you know that with the lowering of the wheels, you will be on the ground shortly. Despite your earlier doubts, you now have supreme confidence in the flight crew. Why shouldn't you? Don't they work for one of the largest airlines in the world? Aren't they constantly monitored and checked by the FAA? Haven't they done this a million times before? You complacently entrust your life to the two people sitting in the pointed end of the airplane.

Now only three miles from the end of the runway, the flight is still too high and too fast for a normally stabilized final approach. This forces the captain to keep the power levers against the idle stops with the nose of the aircraft pointed earthward at a much-steeper-than-normal attitude. With very few lights showing in the approach corridor, it is virtually impossible for the captain to accurately judge his height above the runway. Alignment with the centerline of the runway is also a task that he barely has under control due to the strong, gusty crosswind. The captain once again briefly considers abandoning the approach, but the thunderstorms are now so close to the airport that he would probably be forced to fly through them if he initiated a missed approach. That would almost certainly prove to be fatal. At this point, the best option is to continue to the runway. Although you don't know it, the flight is committed to attempting to land.

Three miles from the end of the runway, the first officer asks the captain for the third time if he wants her to run the before-landing checklist. This should have been accomplished at least five miles from touchdown, but the confusion reigning in the cockpit, the rushed approach, the turbulence and the impairment of both pilots have pushed this vital task down the priority list. In a rather dazed and distracted voice, the captain finally responds to his copilot's inquiries and asks for the checklist. She runs through it without waiting for the captain's normal response to each item on the list. She has no choice. You are now only thirty-seconds from touchdown.

Unfortunately, in her haste, the first officer has inadvertently missed a critical item on the before-landing checklist. In the MD-80, it is standard procedure to place the ground-spoiler-activation lever in the "auto" position so that the ground spoilers will deploy automatically upon spin-up of the main-landing-gear wheels. These relatively small panels on the upper surfaces of both wings serve to dump lift from the airfoil when deployed. With the lift on the wings drastically reduced, the weight of the airplane is transferred from the wing to the wheels, thereby greatly increasing the effectiveness of the brakes.

The ground spoilers can still be deployed manually, but the crew will have to recognize the fact that they have not deployed automatically, react quickly to the situation and then reach over and manually pull a lever on the pedestal aft. Of course, the airplane will be greedily eating up valuable runway every second that the deployment is delayed. This seemingly minor oversight has just added another critical link to the error chain that can lead to an accident.

At a point only one-mile from the end of the runway, the captain decides that the airplane is now on the proper glide slope for the runway. He rapidly advances the power levers to stabilize the descent rate and pitches the nose up in an attempt to reduce the airspeed—he is still forty-knots faster than he should be at this point. Without electronic- or visual-glideslope guidance, however, he can not tell that he is in reality over three-hundred-feet too high. The crosswind is forcing him to keep the nose of the aircraft pointed several degrees into the wind to compensate for the induced drift, and it is almost impossible to keep the wings from rolling to an alarming angle.

With the airplane passing over the end of the runway, you can see patches of water on a taxiway and it looks like it is raining heavily. It doesn't really seem to matter though, since you are almost on the ground. Despite the ordeal you have been through today, you still marvel at the ability of the crew to even find the runway under these conditions. A vision of you warmly hugging your spouse and children suddenly pops into your mind. It won't be long now.

The captain is making his final moves to get the airplane safely on the ground. When the landing lights pick up the runway surface, he immediately realizes that there is standing water on the runway and that he is much too high for a normal landing. A quick glance at his airspeed indicator tells him that he is at least twenty-knots too fast and that the gusts are causing his speed to fluctuate by twenty-knots in a fraction of a second. The nose is still pointed off to the right of the runway centerline and the turbulence has diminished only slightly.

The captain knows that he should go around. The water on the runway will considerably decrease the braking action once the airplane is on the ground. The aircraft's height above the runway and the excessive airspeed will cause the touchdown point to be much further down the runway than desired. He has only a split-second to make his decision. A bolt of lightning strikes the ground at the far end of the runway. This makes up his mind for him. He closes the throttles and dives for the runway.

Sitting in the back of the airplane, you can hardly feel the wheels touch the runway. In fact, it is the smoothest touchdown you have ever experienced. You are certain that the copilot is on the radio to the tower right this second, asking them to verify that the airplane has really landed. A collective sigh of relief is emitted by the passengers. Cheers and clapping break out. After a very hair-raising experience, you are all finally down safely. It is, you think, real security after all.

Up in the cockpit, things are not quite so jubilant. The captain is still wrestling with the airplane as it hurtles down the runway. He has barely managed to place the main landing gear on the narrow runway due to a sudden gust of wind that struck the airplane from the side just before it touched down. The touchdown point is way too far down the runway due to the fact that the airplane was high and fast over the runway threshold. Although satisfyingly smooth to the passengers, the captain realizes that the feather-light touchdown is not a good thing in this situation.

He knows that the aircraft's tires are now hydroplaning. The smooth touchdown has prevented the tires from making solid contact with the surface of the runway—they are now gliding smoothly over a very thin sheet of water. The tires will provide exactly zero braking action. The gentleness of the touchdown also indicates to him that the ground spoilers have not deployed automatically. If they had, he would have felt a solid jolt as they dumped the wings' lift and literally dropped the whole airplane about a foot.

As the realization sinks in that he is now riding a very large sled down a very slick, too-short runway with very little control, the captain reaches over and deploys the ground spoilers manually. The airplane immediately settles down on the landing-gear struts, putting the entire weight of the airplane on the wheels.

Immediately following the deployment of the ground spoilers, he moves his right hand to the reverser levers and lifts them up and back. As he does, more fuel is fed to the engines, thereby increasing their output of power dramatically. While the engines are spooling up, various diverter panels, air ducts and valves are moving into the proper positions in the engine cowlings to deliver reverse thrust to help slow the airplane down. When the engines reach peak power, the airplane starts to yaw to the right. Under these conditions, the airplane wants to weathervane into the wind due to the reverse thrust and the lack of friction at the point-of-contact with the runway. If something isn't done very soon, the airplane will exit the hard-surfaced runway and start plowing through cacti, sagebrush and sand.

Although the captain has never experienced this phenomenon before, he has heard about it. He knows the only thing he can do to keep the airplane from running off the right side of the runway is to take the engines out of reverse thrust and apply full-left rudder.

The sudden decrease in engine noise brings you to attention immediately. After riding through countless airliner landings, you know that the pilots normally keep the engines in reverse until the airplane has slowed down considerably. Hearing them come out of reverse so quickly alerts you to the fact that things might not be going so smoothly after all. A quick look out the window shows that the runway lights are still zipping past at an alarming rate of speed. What is going on? Will the captain be able to stop the airplane before it goes off the end of the runway?

It's working! The captain allows himself a micro-second of relief as the nose of the airplane comes back around to the left. Although the airplane is now very close to the right edge of the runway, the centerline of the airplane is aligned with the runway's center stripe. Maybe this is going to work out yet. He gingerly increases reverse thrust, not daring to let the nose swing even a few degrees to the right. If it does, the airplane will slide off the side of the runway in a heartbeat.

The lights at the end of the runway are rapidly approaching. The captain tromps down on the brake pedals with all his strength and yells for the first officer to do the same. Since the tires touched the runway, she has been merely a wide-eyed passenger along for the ride. There is really nothing else she can do. Any landing, especially a landing in these conditions, is strictly a one-person job. All she can do is root for the captain and standby to assist as directed.

It soon becomes evident to the captain and first officer that the airplane is going to go off the end of the runway at an angle of approximately forty-five degrees from its centerline. The first officer calls out an indicated airspeed of one-hundred knots as the airplane passes over the numbers painted near the runway's end. The airplane is slowing very little because the tires, which normally would have been providing virtually all of the braking energy at this point, are slipping on the now-rain-slicked paint that has been used to mark the runway.

In the split second it takes for the airplane to go off the end of the runway, the captain finds that he has time to reflect upon his aeronautical sins. They are multiple. Not the least of them is the fact that he has landed long and fast on a short, slick runway, in a very-strong crosswind. This is a major aeronautical no-no. Add to that the fact that he has violated several other rules that every professional pilot knows are written in blood, and paid for with many lives.

As the captain feels the landing gear begin to collapse as it enters the soft sand off the end of the runway, he knows that he isn't going to walk away from this one unscathed. The thoughts uppermost in his mind have to deal with how he is going to explain his decisions to the accident-investigation board. It is a funny thing to be thinking at a time like this. He almost laughs, but the sudden appearance of a cement-block building directly in the airliner's path freezes him with fright.

The headlong rush into the wall appears to be happening in slow motion. Now the captain is just another passenger along for the ride. There are only two differences between him and the trusting people riding behind him in this now-doomed, once-graceful flying machine—he is going to be the first to arrive at the scene of the accident and they had nothing to say about the decisions that sealed their collective fate.

✈

You sit bolt upright in seat 33D as the airplane exits the safety of the runway for the terror-filled no-man's-land lurking in the darkness. Although you don't know it, you are experiencing *negative panic*. This is a well-documented psychological state where you are in such a condition of fright that you can't move. You are frozen in place, not even thinking about survival strategies.

As the airplane rolls off the hard surface of the runway, it decelerates rapidly. It feels like the airplane has just rolled into a pit of quicksand. You are thrown forward viciously. Since the pitch between seats in coach has been gradually reduced by the airlines until you can't even bend over to touch your shoes, there is not enough room to bend over to avoid being seriously injured in a crash.

Your face is smashed into the back of the seat in front of you. You, the seatback and the passenger sitting in that seat are all simultaneously thrust forward. Your torso comes to a sudden stop as the passenger in front of you reaches full compression. At the same time, you feel a crushing weight on your back. The passenger behind you has just copied your face-first nose dive. Due to the crash-induced g-forces, the passenger on top of you is exerting a force of almost twelve times his body weight. The air is forced from your lungs as you gasp for life-sustaining oxygen.

The soft earth is clutching the airplane's six tires in its adhesive grip. The landing-gear struts cannot withstand the wrenching force. The nose-wheel strut collapses first, followed within milliseconds by the main struts. Without its supporting legs, the airplane crashes into the ground with a tremendous force. Although you are barely conscious and in a state of panic, you feel the blow to the back of your body as the overhead-storage bins, which contain a tremendous weight of carry-on baggage, are ripped loose from the airframe and hurled down upon you.

Everything is moving in super-slow motion now. You can feel the airplane grinding to a halt. There is a sudden jolt as the airplane crashes into, and comes to rest in, the cement-block building. The captain has experienced this scene as his last conscious thought.

For a moment, everything is quiet. As if awakening from a dream, you hear moans, screams and pleas for help all around you. At first, you can't move. You tentatively try to extricate yourself from your seat by twisting sideways and pushing up with all your might. You still can't move. The overhead bin has you trapped and there is something wrong with your body—it doesn't seem to be able to respond to your commands.

You can't see a thing. It is pitch-black in the cabin. This time, for some unknown reason, as you struggle to free yourself, the overhead bin slips sideways just enough to allow you to move a little. You try to force yourself to your left, but there is an immovable, soft mass lying inertly next to you. It must be the linebacker in the aisle seat. Is he dead?

You yell for him to get out of your way. There is no response. You reach over to push him out of your way and your hands are immediately covered in something sticky. Is it blood? You realize you have to unfasten your seatbelt if you are going to have any chance of getting out. After fumbling with the seatbelt buckle with your blood-soaked hands for what seems like several minutes, you finally release it.

The small boy sitting on your right is now screaming for his mother. You would like to comfort him and tell him that everything is going to be OK—just like you frequently do for your son when he is in distress. However, you know that would be just a waste of time. To help him, you must first extricate yourself.

Now that you are free of your seatbelt, your body falls to your left. The fuselage must be tipped in that direction, but in the darkness of the now-chaotic cabin you can't tell which way is up or out. You struggle over the body of the man in the aisle seat. As you reach up to touch his face in an attempt to find signs of life, you discover a horrific fact—his head is missing. How can that be? Something must have flown forward from the galley area and decapitated him. Rather than revolting you, the stark realization that you are now climbing over a headless man only galvanizes you with an intense desire to get out of the airplane.

As you try to steady yourself on the tilted aisle floor, you reach back over the man in the aisle seat and grab the boy by his arm. You pull him towards you. He screams and tries to tear his arm away. Falling backwards, you lose him in the darkness and confusion. People are pushing at you from both sides, yelling for you to get out of their way. You ignore their pleas and try to determine which way is out. There are cries for help everywhere.

Suddenly, you see a dim, flickering light in the forward part of the cabin. You can see a flight attendant struggling to open the forward entry door, but it seems to be stuck. You don't have time to analyze the situation. If you did, you would quickly figure out that the door is being held closed because the airplane has rolled onto its left side making it impossible to get that door open. The flight attendant is repeatedly yelling for everyone to unfasten their seatbelts and get out while she continues to struggle with the door.

Since you had long ago given up on watching the flight attendants perform their pre-takeoff briefing, you have no clear idea of where the other exits are. You now wish that you had paid more attention. As you try to figure out what to do next, the meager light that you had seen in the front of the cabin suddenly goes out. You are plunged back into total darkness.

You turn around, hoping to see some clue that will tell you where a life-saving exit might be. You abruptly smell smoke. The first acrid tendrils to reach your nostrils cause only a minor irritation, but as you take a breath through your mouth, your throat starts to constrict. You can't breath. All your attempts to draw life-giving air into your lungs are futile. You have drawn your last breath. A thought creeps into your mind as you slowly loose consciousness. It was false security after all.

Chapter 5: "Air Travelers' Heaven"

"A sky as pure as water
bathed the stars
and brought them out."
                Antoine de Saint-Exupéry
                "Southern Mail"

You sense that you are floating serenely in the free-fall of space. A feeling of satisfaction and joy permeates your soul as you take pleasure in the affection of a family group hug. It's nice to be home, especially after that horrendous airline flight.

"Wait a minute," you think. "Didn't the airplane I was in crash? Wasn't I trapped in the cabin?" You recall a horrifying scene of broken bodies, blood, cries for help, the sweet-acrid smell of burning jet fuel and the terrible swelling in your throat as life-giving air is choked from your searing lungs. The realization of what has just happened to you forces its way into your mind—you died in that crash!

This appalling thought causes your eyelids to snap wide open. You are not safely at home with your loved ones after all. A vague image swims before you. It takes some time for you to focus your eyes and start to make some sense of your surroundings. Although you seem to have tunnel vision, the picture directly in front of you becomes clear. You are amazed at what you see. It is a vision of a secluded beach on a tropical isle. Your point of view is from a small boat making its way over the breakers and into a picture-perfect lagoon. Music seems to engulf you and the sound of the waves crashing against the beach reaches your consciousness. You feel a gentle, pitching motion in your body. You are warm and comfortable. "How did I get here? Is this heaven?" you ask.

As your field of view widens, you discover, to your surprise, that you are not in a small boat approaching an island. The boat, the island and the water are images on a video screen. The monitor is mounted on an arm that is attached to the aircraft seat you are sitting in. The sounds you are hearing are entering your ears through a light-weight headset, and the motion you feel is generated by the airplane you are in as it glides smoothly through a disturbance in the surrounding atmosphere. "I must be in an airplane! Maybe I didn't die. Perhaps it was just a hideous dream after all," you think. Hope rushes back into your soul.

You become more fully awake and aware of your surroundings. You are sitting in the cabin of a jet that is unlike any airliner you have ever been in. It appears to be a bizjet—one of those corporate barges that only the very rich can afford. The window seat in which you are sitting is spacious and very comfortable. You have the seatback reclined to a comfortable angle and you can feel the whole seat massaging you. Your legs are supported by a footrest that has been extended from below your calves. The back of the seat in front of you seems to be a par-five-drive away.

The cabin itself is pleasingly large with no overhead bins to make it feel small and cramped. You look around and discover that there are only eighteen seats in the cabin, not the typical cattle-car seating you've become accustomed to in the airliners you normally fly on. There are pleasant looking people sitting comfortably in most of the seats.

The seats are arranged in such a way as to maximize the spaciousness of the cabin. Each seat has plenty of room, and the latest in video-and-audio-entertainment systems are at your fingertips. In the back of the cabin, you can see a well-stocked galley and a spacious lavatory. A glance out your window reveals a panorama of sky and clouds. You are cruising high above the weather in a cerulean sky. Not a worry in the world. "But what world is this? Is this heaven, or am I still alive?" you ask out loud, not really expecting an answer.

"Well, my friend, you are certainly *not* alive in the same sense that you were a short time ago, and let me assure you that this *is* heaven and not the less-desirable alternative." These words seem to float into your left ear. The language is English, but it is spoken with a heavy French accent. Are you imagining the voice, or is it real? You slowly turn your head to your left and notice for the first time that someone is sitting next to you. It is not the linebacker. "Where did he come from?" you silently ask yourself.

Your seatmate is a middle-aged gentleman dressed in fashionable leisure wear. He is peering into your eyes with a steady gaze. A look of pleasant amusement is on his face. His eyes draw you in and you notice that there are spectacular crow's-feet at their outer corners. He is extremely fit and he exudes a powerful aura of command, self confidence and goodwill. His overall aspect strongly suggests that he is a man who has sailed all seven seas and flown around the world more times than Sputnik. He sits patiently, waiting for you to say something.

"Where am I and who are you?" is the best you can manage. He smiles pleasantly and says, "You are in Air Travelers' Heaven and I am Fleet Commander Antoine de Saint-Exupéry, but you can call me Antoine." You think he must be kidding you. What the devil is an 'Air Travelers' Heaven' and what's a 'fleet commander' anyway? Antoine reaches over and firmly grasps your right hand.

"Welcome, we have been expecting you," Antoine begins. "I am here to brief you on your new world. Think of me as your guide. Now, sit back and relax and I'll make everything clear for you. Would you like a drink?"

You suddenly recall the pain of your smoke-constricted throat and you unsteadily murmur, "Yes, I would." Antoine glides gracefully to the galley in the rear of the cabin. He returns a short time later with a drink in his hand.

"Here," he says, "you certainly look like you need this, my dear fellow. Now, let me begin by telling you all about myself. It is a good thing we have all the time we need as I thoroughly enjoy speaking of my exploits," Antoine cheerfully exclaims with a wry smile.

As you sip your drink— you notice it's wonderful—Antoine begins his tale. "I was born in France in 1900. I was shot out of the sky by the Hun while flying over the Mediterranean during World War II. The year was 1944. I unfortunately died in the ensuing crash," he explains.

"Wait a minute," you quickly interject. "What do you mean you died in 1944? How can that be?"

Antoine's reply gives you that dreaming feeling once again. "Yes, I died as did you. We are both safely and pleasantly ensconced in Air Travelers' Heaven—or as we prefer to say in the fleet, A-T-H."

"Air Travelers' Heaven, ATH, what in the world is he talking about?" you think.

Antoine regards you with a serene countenance and tells you, "Yes, I can read your mind, and if you will be so kind as to give me your full attention, I will soon answer every question to your complete satisfaction. *Bon*?"

His story is amazing. Antoine, Fleet Commander Antoine de Saint-Exupéry, was one of the great pioneers of early aviation. In the 1920s, he flew the mail on his regular run from Toulouse, France to Dakar, Senegal. His adventures are legendary. In addition to his skills as an aviator, Antoine has written several very popular books and poems such as *"The Little Prince"* and *"Wind, Sand and Stars"*. Many feel he is one of the greatest writers of all time. His philosophical musings on aviation, the world and the state of humanity are widely quoted and admired.

Antoine finishes his personal tale by saying, "And when I arrived here in ATH in 1944, I was soon after anointed as Fleet Commander and given the privilege of greeting all new arrivals with a thorough briefing on their new universe." These last words shake you.

"New universe?" you ask.

"Yes," Antoine whispers, "new universe. It will go much easier for you if you merely accept your fate. You died in that airline crash in your old universe and now you have been reborn in this one." With these words, a calm feeling infuses your body and you acknowledge for the first time that you may have really died and gone to Air Travelers' Heaven.

Antoine senses that you are now ready for a full explanation of your destiny. You relax in your seat and take a large swallow of your drink.

"That's funny," you think, "this drink is still full and I've been swigging it repeatedly."

"That is not the only thing you cannot run out of here in ATH." Antoine points out. "But, we will address that matter a little later," he promises.

Antoine begins your briefing by telling you that when air travelers die, they go to either Air Travelers' Heaven or Air Travelers' Hell. "It all depends upon the state of your spirit at the time of your death," he tells you.

According to Antoine, if you were a real air-travel enthusiast in your prior existence, and if you had suffered the proper level of pain, suffering and indignation in the air-travel system of that world, you would ascend to Air Travelers' Heaven when you died. And if you died in an airplane crash, your chances of being reborn in ATH were increased several fold.

"It is much like Golfers' Heaven or Fishermens' Heaven for aficionados of those pursuits," Antoine postulates. "However, if in that other realm you were not enthusiastic and gracious in your air-travel adventures, you might well be relegated to Air Travelers' Hell for the rest of time."

"OK, Antoine," you say, "we're in Air Travelers' Heaven and this seems to be pretty nice, but what is Air Travelers' Hell like?"

Antoine responds, "To understand Air Travelers' Hell, one must simply take a look at the air travel system in your previous world in the year 2010. Of course you know what it is like now, and if you will kindly direct your attention to your video monitor I will show you what Air Travelers' Hell is like, my friend."

Your brow furrows. How could air travel in 2010 be any worse than it was in your time? Weren't the airlines and the government making promises almost every day that the national air-transportation system was going to dramatically improve? Of course, the bureaucrats that ran the airlines and the FAA were claiming that the change for the better would be due to their efforts on your behalf.

Divining your thoughts once again, Antoine proclaims "If you believe that the bureaucrats are going to help you, my good-natured traveler, then I have some water-front property near Tucson, Arizona that I would like to sell to you. It is a well-known fact within the aviation industry that your Federal Aviation Administration has *never*, please let me repeat the word *never*, met an important project deadline. Most insiders believe they never will. Now, please pay close attention to your television monitor."

The first images to appear on your video screen are of a terminal building that is obviously over twenty-years old. It is swarming with people pushing and shoving as they fight to move through the jam-packed concourses. A text-graphic is rolling across the bottom of the screen explaining that no new airport infrastructure has been built between 2002 and 2010 while the number of passengers trying to transit these antiquated structures has more than doubled.

The bureaucrats' excuse is that airline profits and tax revenues have been down ever since the terrorist attack on the World Trade Center in 2001. Therefore, they have been disingenuously explaining, there hasn't been enough money to improve landside facilities. Whatever the reason was for the lack of terminal expansion in the years following your death, it is obvious that trying to navigate the jammed airline terminals of 2010 is all but impossible. You immediately see that Antoine is right. What you are viewing on the monitor really is Air Travelers' Hell.

The next view is of the interior of a relatively new airliner. There are over 1,000 passengers stuffed into the huge amphitheater-like cabin. Although the airplane is much bigger than the airliners of your day, it is even more crowded. "How in the world can all those people get out of that airplane quickly in the event of a crash?" your recent experience with airline crashes prompts you to ask.

"They can't," Antoine replies, "it takes them the better part of an hour to enplane or deplane in the best of circumstances."

"And speaking of air crashes," Antoine says, "in the year 2010 in your old universe, the airlines of the world are averaging slightly over one airline crash per week."

You nearly jump out of your seat. "What do you mean over one crash per week? How can that be?" you ask.

"It was inevitable," Antoine patiently explains. "It is a simple mathematical computation. If you take the number of air crashes in 2002 and increase them in direct relation to the increase in the number of airline flights by 2010, you can easily see that at least one crash each week results. Of course, the bureaucrats of 2002 promised vast improvements in air safety, but they never came about because maintaining the airlines' bottom line and their positions of power were more important to them than the lives of others."

"This is terrible," you think. What would it be like having to put your mortal soul aboard an airliner knowing full well that at least one of these marvels of high technology would fall out of the sky that very week? It was bad enough in your time when major air crashes were becoming commonplace already. You could see that it truly would be Hell if you had to subject yourself and your loved ones to that kind of uncertainty and stress on a frequent basis. "After all," you say, "who wants to play 'Russian Roulette' that often?"

As your mind reels from the idea of leading such a risky and stressful air-traveler's life, Antoine redirects your attention to the video screen. "And look at this my friend," he suggests while pointing to the rapidly flowing images of hundreds of airplanes lined up for takeoff and scores more circling in holding patterns waiting for landing clearance.

"Here again we have a case of the bureaucrats' negligence," he says. "They did not move fast enough with air-traffic-control-system and airport improvements to keep up with the wildly expanding demand for air travel. Their neglect has led to multi-hour saturation-induced delays at their hub airports on a continuous basis. In the year 2010, the portal-to-portal time for travel by air in the United States has gone up so dramatically that it is faster to drive than to fly if your destination is less than one-thousand-miles away."

"So, do you not agree, my comrade, is this not in fact Air Travelers' Hell?" Antoine asks as he smiles and looks at you expectantly. "And if you don't believe it yet, I can supply many more examples of how the airline system of 2010 resembles a living hell."

You have to agree. If air travel has really gotten as bad as it appears, it will in fact be hell to have to travel in that system on a regular basis.

"But enough of this doom and gloom," Antoine cheerily announces. "Let us instead think about Air Travelers' Heaven. I am sure you will find that to be much more pleasant." You heartily concur.

"First of all," Antoine begins, "let me enlighten you as to how time works in parallel universes. You see, the cosmic clockworks of all possible universes seem to be inextricably synchronized. Therefore, no matter which universe you may find yourself in, time will be synchronized and move along at the same pace. For example, you died only a few minutes ago in your previous mortal existence. Now you are alive in this universe only a few minutes later. There has been a continuum of the timeline. It has remained perfectly matched in both universes."

"I see," you tentatively respond, not really sure that you understand at all. "But then, how can Air Travelers' Heaven be so different from the world of air travel in my other life?" you ask.

"I said only that the timelines of that world and this are synchronized. I did not mean to imply that the history embedded in those two timelines is identical. On the contrary, they have been very different," Antoine explains.

"Wait a second," you blurt out. "I can buy that, I guess, but how can we see the future in my other world displayed in the video-entertainment system?"

"Easily explainable," Antoine offers. "But that is a story that will have to wait a little while longer. For now, just let me say that in Air Travelers' Heaven, many things are possible and that is only one of them. Please, my friend, for the moment, just accept the fact that in ATH we can look backward and forward along the infinite timelines of all universes. This, I am afraid, has been both a blessing and a curse, but we will talk of these matters at another time." You readily agree to leave the cosmological discussion for the layover and quietly await Antoine's next surprise. You are not disappointed.

"So, my very-bright pupil, what are your questions?" Antoine invites.

"OK. Tell me all about Air Travelers' Heaven. What's it like? How did air travel evolve so differently in this world? Who thought of this concept anyway? Please Antoine. Tell me everything."

"With pleasure," he replies.

Chapter 6: "The Power"

"In the face of overpowering mystery,
you don't dare disobey."

                    Antoine de Saint-Exupéry
                    "The Little Prince"

"Let us commence," Antoine begins, "at the point in time in your old universe and in this one when the evolution of air travel diverged. It was the year 1992. At that time, in both worlds, air travel was continuing along the trajectory it had been on since the deregulation of the industry in the year 1979. By 1992, thanks to the cleverness of computer-based yield-management systems, almost everyone in the developed world in both universes had been able to afford an airline ticket and travel somewhere on a modern jet airliner at least once."

"However, this unprecedented mobility that was being enjoyed by humankind was dearly paid for. By this time, only thirteen years after deregulation of the airline industry, the system was so clogged up that actual portal-to-portal travel times started to get longer, reversing a trend that had been progressing smoothly in the direction of shorter-and-shorter travel times during all of the prior recorded history of the human race. Also, air travel had become very frustrating, uncomfortable, inconvenient and unreliable."

"It was in that year, 1992, that a few very experienced air-travel enthusiasts in this universe decided that there had to be a better way to fly. I was fortunate to be among that small group of people who decided to make our air-travel system in this universe faster, safer, more convenient and more comfortable for more people."

"You see, we were all fed up with an airline management corps that frequently lied to us about the level of safety that was economically viable. We also believed that it was unconscionable for those managers to focus their attention on the value of their stock options instead of the well-being of people who had placed their lives in their hands. They should have been providing their customers with an air-transportation system that was improving rather than one that was unraveling into chaos."

"We wanted to change things for the better because we were, you see, addicted to air travel. It had become a way of life for many of us. And the sheer pleasure of it—when we took a few minutes to gaze out the cabin windows—provided our harried souls with a sense of peace, unbounded power and our place in the universe."

"We all wanted to jet about the world arriving as quickly as possible at our final destination. We also sought to do this in style and comfort, and we wanted the system to be as safe and convenient as is humanly possible. We had no desire to live for all eternity in a world where air travel was becoming increasingly slower and unpleasant."

"The people running the airlines at that time believed that the traveling public wanted the cheapest possible seats. On the other hand, we knew that there was a significant share of those people who were smart enough to realize that they could, in many cases, pay a little more for airfare, and at the same time significantly reduce the overall, fully allocated costs of getting from 'A' to 'B'. We were certain that those savvy travelers would see that not only could they lower their overall cost of air travel, but they could also enjoy faster portal-to-portal travel times while taking pleasure in the knowledge that their journey was safer and more convenient."

"It was my great pleasure to bring these air-travel enthusiasts together in this universe," Antoine explains. "I pointed out to them how their diverse talents and experience in aviation and business could come together to create very positive changes if they would only align themselves and focus their incredible collective expertise on a common goal."

"I need not have worried myself on this account," Antoine admits, "for they were already well versed in the employment of these little-used, but most-powerful, of human capabilities— alignment and focus. They quickly formed a close-knit working group and proceeded to design a new future for air travelers. It is this vision of how air travel was truly meant to be that we call Air Travelers' Heaven."

"The bedrock of this new air-travel paradigm was the idea that a well-informed group of people who were allied and motivated by self interest could, from the resources that were available to them at that time, craft an air-travel system that was safe, affordable and vastly more pleasant to travel in than the one provided by airline management. They created the foundation for their new venture by simply bringing together a significant number of the air-travel enthusiasts who had grown weary of the delays, frustrations and mounting safety concerns of the old system."

"How did they do that?" you ask.

Antoine replies, "They did this by first publishing a book that turned out to be very popular among air-travel enthusiasts. The book laid out the then-current problems with the air travel system and described in detail how those problems could be solved through the alignment of the members of this group. It also revealed the plan for creating Air Travelers' Heaven."

"After reading the book, most serious air travelers went to the group's Web site for more information on how to make it all happen. There they found more information and were invited to join others who believed that they really could change the air-travel system for the better."

"Once these air-travel enthusiasts were communicating with each other, a process was initiated that ultimately united them in their pursuit of Air Travelers' Heaven. The founders knew that this critical alignment process could be completed because they had accomplished similar tasks with large numbers of individuals many times in the past. They also knew that once this alignment was achieved, a very powerful force for change could be focused on the areas that were critical to the establishment of Air Travelers' Heaven."

"The vehicles they used to focus this collective power were a simple limited liability company and two non-profit organizations. The limited liability company handled the creation of an air-transportation system that would fulfill the desire of the group for a better way to fly. They named the company Universal Aerospacelines, or UA."

"One of the non-profits concentrated on public awareness, advocacy and political action focused on improving the existing air-travel infrastructure. They called it Air Travelers United, or ATU. The other organization worked on the long-range plans and goals that the group shared. This was christened The Human Trust, or THT."

"A unique aspect of their UA business model was their insistence that everyone involved in the venture participate simultaneously in three normally separate roles," Antoine reveals. "Of course, these three roles exist in every business venture. They are the roles of customer, owner and operator. The founders defined 'operator' as an employee of the company, a vendor to the company, a consultant or advisor to the company or an independent contractor to the company—someone who serves the customers of the company either directly or indirectly."

"What was different in this case," Antoine continues, "was the fact that for the first time, each individual within the organization would be required to play all three roles at the same time. This one insight was enough to ensure the success of their endeavor. You see, by insisting that everyone participate fully in all three roles simultaneously, a very powerful dynamic is set in motion that miraculously removes the factors that always, over time, corrode the bonds that hold people together."

"In Air Travelers' Heaven, the founders believed, there would be no unhealthy power struggles. The founders realized that inevitably, in a traditional business model, factions are set against one another by the forces of greed and envy. In Air Travelers' Heaven, gone would be the days of labor-management strife and employee-customer friction. This new air-travel paradigm, they believed, would be a place that would certainly deserve the name of Air Travelers' Heaven."

"Incredible, I can see it!" you exclaim. "The combination of alignment and the enlightened self-interest of putting yourself into all three of the key roles at the same time are marvelous. It's pure genius!" It is now obvious to you that the new venture couldn't miss. It was bound to be successful.

"This is great Antoine," you proclaim. "How could anyone fail with a business strategy like that?"

"They could not and they did not," Antoine answers. "But there is more—much, much more."

"Please continue," you say as you lean in closer to Antoine and focus your full attention on what he is about to say.

Antoine elegantly rearranges himself in his seat and continues the story. "They also designed into their business model a means for avoiding the very dangerous pitfalls that result from being bottom-line driven in a safety-sensitive business."

"You see, since the early days following deregulation of the airline industry, airline managers have been flying their companies into what pilots refer to as a 'graveyard spiral'. By competing with each other on the basis of 'least-cost' rather than 'most value', they are forced to continually eliminate from their cost structure any safety and convenience improvements that are not mandated by the government."

"And since the government gives more weight to the airlines' pleas for lower costs than to air travelers' demands for improvements to the system, it is not likely to tell the airline managers to pull out of their headlong corkscrew into the ground. Besides, what bureaucracy ever implemented system improvements if they would, in the end, cost it funding, staffing and power. It appeared to the founders of Air Travelers' Heaven that the old system was doomed to get worse and worse until it failed completely. They knew they had to take matters into their own hands and facilitate, as quickly as possible, their ascension from Air Travelers' Hell to Air Travelers' Heaven."

"How in this world, or any other for that matter, did they do that?" you ask.

"They based their business model on a soaring arc instead of a graveyard spiral," he replies. "Their standard for investing in improvements to UA's operations was simple: if an investment would improve the safety, speed, convenience and/or comfort of the system at a cost that did not put airfares out of reach of the people using the system, the investment was made. In other words, instead of sacrificing improvements on the altar of 'cheapest seats', they built a better system with their focus on 'highest value'. You see, they did not think solely of the bottom line. They were free to concentrate instead on safety and service."

"Air Travelers' Heaven's founders also had the foresight to build into their business model a means of retaining the market share they knew they were sure to wrest from the airlines," Antoine states. "It was highly unusual then, over ten years ago, for a company to plan to retain its market share even before it entered business. In fact, it is still rare but it has worked, how do you say, 'like a charm'. Today, UA's market-share is stable and new members are waiting in line to join."

"But what did they do to retain their share of the air-travel market?" you ask.

Antoine replies, "Ah, my friend that is a closely guarded secret known only to those who enjoy citizenship in Air Travelers' Heaven. I am afraid that until you choose to join them, I am not at liberty to reveal it to you."

Up to this point, you had not realized that you were going to have to make a decision to become an Air Travelers' Heaven citizen. You thought that by virtue of the fact that you were already in Air Travelers' Heaven, you would be able to continue to enjoy the wonders of this new universe without any further effort on your part.

You turn to Antoine and ask, "What do you mean I have to choose to be an Air Travelers' Heaven citizen? I thought that since I was already in Air Travelers' Heaven, I would automatically be an Air Travelers' Heaven inhabitant."

"I regret that this is not so my friend," Antoine laments. "You must consider this merely an introductory flight and briefing. Although you certainly appear to qualify for Air Travelers' Heaven citizenship—you are an air-travel enthusiast and you travel by air frequently—I am afraid that there is more to it than that."

"Like what?" you query.

"Well, to begin with, you must be in alignment with Air Travelers' Heaven's vision, goals, plans and policies. You must also commit to playing all three of the roles required of you—owner, customer and operator. Then there is the matter of your financial commitment. Are you prepared and willing to transfer to your Air Travelers' Heaven air-travel account the money that you now give to the ungrateful airlines for their substandard air travel services?"

"How much money are we talking about?" you ask.

"As you Americans are so fond of saying, the bottom line is what counts," Antoine replies. "If you add up all of your air-travel costs in Air Travelers' Heaven, you will find that they will be less than your total costs for purchasing airline travel."

"Now, if you want to include the tremendous gains in personal productivity that result from the air-travel system in Air Travelers' Heaven, the value you receive for your air-travel expenditures soars, if you will pardon the expression, out of this world. If all the many hours that you save in portal-to-portal travel time in Air Travelers' Heaven are added together, you can easily see that you have much more time for your personal life. Of course, if you choose, you can also devote that time to your work. In either case, when you combine the time savings with the increased ability to work in flight that is available aboard the aircraft in Air Travelers' Heaven, you can see that your life will be much more productive."

"Well Antoine," you allow, "this deal sounds like a no-brainer to me. Where do I sign up?"

"Please restrain your ponies my dear friend," Antoine pleads. "Although you are certainly qualified for Air Travelers' Heaven citizenship, and you apparently are prepared to make the required financial commitment, you have not as yet indicated to me that you are in alignment with Air Travelers' Heaven's vision, goals and plans. Alas, you have not yet committed to playing all the requisite roles demanded of an Air Travelers' Heaven citizen. You must first do all this before I may sponsor you for citizenship."

"Sponsorship?" you query. "Are you telling me that I can't just join Air Travelers' Heaven on my own?"

"I am afraid not my friend," Antoine replies. "You see, all new citizens must be sponsored by an existing citizen before they are allowed to join us in what you yourself are now referring to as Air Travelers' Heaven. You may think of it as the aeronautical version of a country club."

"Since, as your sponsor, I must be convinced that you are one of us, I think it would be best if we take a closer look at the founders' vision, goals and plans next," Antoine asserts.

You reply, "Whatever you say Antoine. You're the boss—or should I say the Fleet Commander?"

"Let us first take up the story of the vision," Antoine suggests. "You see, every triumphant human endeavor must begin with a clear vision of what is to be achieved."

"I couldn't agree more," you state. "But isn't that usually the problem? Isn't that why most people are afraid to join a cause or pursue a goal that appears at first to be not-doable, despite the fact that the idea intrigues them? You know, even though their rational analysis can't find any flaws in the facts and conclusions underlying the call to action, they still hesitate to join because they can't personally *see* a successful outcome."

"Ah, *me ami,*" Antoine utters in reply. "I can now see that you are a philosopher in addition to an air-travel enthusiast."

"Well Antoine, I guess that's because in the world I just came from, if you were an air traveler, you had to be philosophical about things," you say. "It was the only way to survive."

"*Touché!*" Antoine laughs with a wide smile on this handsome face. "Now I see that you are a comedian also. But let us be serious for a moment. I want to show to you Air Travelers' Heaven's vision."

"Please proceed," you respond while quickly composing yourself.

"I have found it useful to begin all discussions of *vision* by defining the term," Antoine suggests. "As you, a philosopher in your own right, know, if people are to achieve an alliance, they must use clearly defined terms in the dialogue leading up to it."

"Let us begin by defining the word *vision*. If you consult *Webster's New World College Dictionary*, you will find that it defines the word as: something supposedly seen by other than normal sight; something perceived in a dream or trance or supernaturally revealed, as to a prophet; a mental image, especially, an imaginative contemplation; the ability to perceive something not actually visible, as through mental acuteness or keen foresight; force or power of imagination."

"So can we not agree that for our purposes, the term *vision* means a clear mental image of the founders' dream of Air Travelers' Heaven? Does not this image have to be viewed with something other than normal sight? Do you not believe that the person seeing the vision must summon up mental acuteness and keen foresight? Is this not the definition of *vision* that we can agree upon?"

"Agreed," you succinctly respond.

"Good," Antoine states. "Now, if you will prepare yourself to see a bright, shining vision of what air travel can be, we will proceed."

"One of the founders of Air Travelers' Heaven, a man you will soon meet, was the incubator of the vision. He harbored the vision for many years after it first appeared to him. He improved upon it from time-to-time and occasionally tested its key elements. The vision may simply have been the result of purely logical thinking and rational deduction, driven by the desire to come up with a viable alternative to airline travel. It might have been the power of the universe speaking directly to him. Who knows? What is known is that the very core of the vision was slowly developing over the course of more than twenty years in the brain, heart and soul of this man."

"And what is at the core of the vision?" you ask eagerly.

"It is nothing less than the survival of the human race," Antoine reveals with a sincere and serious look on his face.

For a moment, you are stunned. You thought you were learning about an alternative to airline travel and Antoine casually asserts that something entirely different is at work here. You wonder how these two ideas fit together.

"OK, Antoine, I'll bite. Tell me how the survival of the human race and a new paradigm in air travel figure into the Air Travelers' Heaven vision."

It's obvious that Antoine has been waiting for just this question. With a benign look on his face, he begins. "The gentleman who originally had the vision of Air Travelers' Heaven had worked in the space program from the mid-1970s through the mid-1980s. A major part of his work was trying to persuade the public to pay more attention to developing the means to leave this planet."

"It was during this time that he determined that the survival of the human race was the highest purpose to which he could dedicate his life. But please, allow me to allow him to tell his own story of the vision. If you would be so kind as to direct your attention to your monitor once again, I will activate the 'play' button."

After a brief period of static and flickering colors, an image appears on the video screen. It is of a wizened male of obviously advanced years. What is left of his hair is thin, gray and pulled straight back from his high forehead. His face sports a benevolent smile, there is a twinkle in his eyes and his cheeks glow with warmth and avuncular goodwill. "He looks a lot like the old man behind the curtain in the Land of Oz," you think. He is sitting in the cockpit of a jet, his body twisted around so that he can look directly at the camera. Through the cockpit windows, you can see a blue sky populated with puffy white clouds.

"Please let me add my welcome to Air Travelers' Heaven," he begins in a soft, baritone voice. "Since Antoine is your sponsor, I know that you will eventually choose to join us. No one does a better job of briefing new arrivals on the Air Travelers' Heaven vision, goals and plans. I know that I have been called upon to share with you our vision and to explain how it was conceived. So let me turn the cockpit over to my relief captain and the first officer and I'll join you in the cabin shortly." The video screen goes dark.

While you are still trying to sort out what just happened, the now-familiar face of your new interlocutor appears in the cockpit door, followed immediately thereafter by his stocky, almost-well-conditioned body. As the captain—you notice he has four gold stripes on the sleeves of his uniform—approaches you, he extends his right hand. You put your hand in his and are greeted by a firm, warm handshake. He is looking directly into your eyes and there is a very friendly countenance portrayed on his face.

"I'm Captain Noah Wiczárd, but my friends all call me simply Noah. So, please do call me Noah yourself," he offers. "Shall we begin?" he asks.

Noah genially waits for you to agree before proceeding. You subtly nod your head, indicating your agreement with the process. He smiles and proceeds to turn the seat in front of you around so it faces you. Sliding the seat towards you a few inches, he stops and latches it, leaving a very comfortable space still between the two seats. He agilely slips into the seat and fastens his seatbelt. You fasten yours also, after looking out the window to confirm that you are still in flight. Every good air traveler knows that it is smart to keep it fastened whenever the airplane is moving.

"Well, where do I begin?" Noah muses as he rubs his chin. "I guess I should begin by telling you that in addition to my enthusiasm for air travel, I've also had an unusually strong addiction to science fiction most of my life. The SciFi habit has abated somewhat, but my passion for flight has grown more intense over the many years that I have been piloting aircraft. We'll talk a lot more about airplanes and air travel in a minute, but let's concentrate on my off-world bent first."

"I don't know when or how my interest in science fiction began, but I do remember that when I was growing up on the farm just about every other program we could tune-in on our black-and-white TV set had to do with space travel and visiting other worlds."

"Of course, that was in the Sputnik era. I think I was ten years old when the Russians launched Sputnik into orbit and shocked the whole world. Walt Disney and his co-conspirator, Dr. Werner von Braun, were having the times of their lives running wild through our young imaginations. They were filling them with crazy ideas like spaceships, orbiting hotels and settlements on the moon. I guess it must have been a cosmic connection that I started reading in earnest around that time."

"I've always been inordinately interested in airplanes since before I can remember. I blame that on TV too. As I recall, we also got a very heavy dose of WW II and Cold War propaganda movies on those old TV sets. I couldn't tell you how many hours of John Wayne fighter-pilot movies were poured into my young and highly impressionable mind. But I can assure you that it was more than enough to make it my life's passion to fly airplanes."

"As I got older, it was only a short hop from airplanes to spaceships, given the milieu in which I grew up. In any event, I've read all the science fiction books I could get my hands on since then. I've read the great authors like Heinlein, Asimov, Clarke and Herbert. I even had the opportunity to personally meet and talk with most of them, and some lesser lights to boot."

"Now, I don't want you to think the only thing I read back then was science-fiction novels," Noah hastily inserts. "I also read the works of Buckminster Fuller, all of Asimov's non-fiction books, Dr. Gerard O'Neil's *'Colonies In Space'* and scores of technical books and studies on spaceflight and off-earth migration."

"I'm telling you about my background so you will be able to understand that, for some unknown reason, I had been prepared for the ready acceptance of my life's mission when it finally made itself known to me. When I came across it—which was another cosmic connection by the way—it jumped right up into my lap. And it has remained my central focus despite more than one attempt to abandon it."

"That's why I still carry it with me today. And I thank the cosmos that I do. It has given my life meaning and it has been a beacon I can home in on when I'm not sure what I should be doing next. I don't know what I'd do without it. In my humble opinion, everyone should have one."

"This story has certainly taken an odd twist," you think. "We started out talking about an alternative to airline travel. Then we veered off onto a discussion of a vision, and now we're talking about a higher purpose and a life's mission."

"I'm confused," you say aloud.

"No need to be," Noah declares. "I know what you're thinking and let me assure you that we will arrive safely at our destination. Just sit back, relax and leave the flying to me. I've done this a couple of times before."

Antoine, who has been sitting quietly in the seat on your left seemingly in a dream world of his own, kindly reaches over and lays his hand on your left forearm. You turn your head to look at him. He smiles and says, "Noah always tells such interesting stories and they are always true, or mostly so at the very least."

Noah guffaws at what is obviously an old jibe softly lobbed from one close friend to another, probably for the thousandth time. Antoine continues, "I would earnestly suggest to you, my friend, that you pay close attention to Noah's tale. It may hold more meaning for you than you can now imagine."

Chapter 7: "The Vision"

"But no one had believed him
on account of the way he was dressed.
Grown-ups are like that."

                    Antoine de Saint-Exupéry
                    "The Little Prince"

     You turn back to face Noah in the seat across from you. He is beaming and noticeably eager to continue his account of how he came upon his life's work. "As I was saying before I was so ungraciously interrupted," Noah jokes and you are sure you detect another one of his winks, "let's get back on course."

     Noah resumes his discourse by saying, "And there I was—at fifty-thousand feet—on my back with my controls shot away by enemy fire—the sky red with tracers, and not a single comic book that I hadn't read. No, wait a minute. That must be another story," he deadpans.

It takes a second for the joke to sink in, but you soon realize that you had been hooked on the hangar tale Noah was telling. Now you can see by the look on his face that he is teasing you. You laugh and bask in the warm glow of knowing that you are being accepted by these two impressive gentlemen.

"Let's get back to the real story," Noah suggests. "There I was. In a downtown-Denver book store," he begins. For a fleeting second you start to think that Noah is once again pulling your leg, but he goes on as if nothing has happened. "It was the winter of 1978 and I was in Denver for training at Bravo X-ray Airline's flight-training center. You see, I was a young, jet-transport flight officer then."

"Anyway, the training had been long and difficult and I was taking a break from my studies on a Sunday afternoon. I had wandered into a used-book store on a shabby side street that appeared to be populated by winos and hippies. Yes, there were still hippies in Denver in those days. Most of them were probably in the book store to warm up. That was my primary motivation for going into the store. I remember that it was bitterly cold and windy that day."

"I can still smell the burning incense and scented candles. Everyone was carrying a steaming cup of the two-bit coffee." The look on your face prompts Noah to quickly interject, "Yes, you couldn't spend more than fifty-cents for a cup of coffee back then—even in a fancy restaurant. Of course, this was before Starbucks!"

Noah returns to the thread of the story, "I had just started to browse the shelves for something interesting when the title of a little book jumped out at me. It was *'Migration To The Stars: Never Again Enough People'* by Edward S. Gilfillan, Jr. Without conscious thought, my hand reached up and snatched it from its place among the books about herbal remedies and meditation. I thought at first it was one of the many books that must surely be in the store that described the planet's growing population problem. You see, at the time, awareness of the world's headlong rush into over-population was probably at its zenith. But why the subtitle *'Never Again Enough People'*?"

"I paid for the book and returned to my room, anxious to find out what it had to tell me. I read it cover-to-cover in one sitting. It turned out that the premise of the book was that humankind's true destiny is to populate the universe. And to do that, there would never again be enough humans to fill up the available environment. The author used mathematical proofs and logic to prove his points. I could find no fault with his arguments."

"Setting the book aside, I pondered the implications of the author's reasoning. By this time, I had been working in the space program for a couple of years as a freelance aerospace journalist and activist for a more-aggressive space-development effort. That experience, and my extensive science-fiction and science-fact reading, had already convinced me that humankind's destiny lay off the planet Earth."

"Like many of my contemporaries, I was certain that humankind would some day migrate off this little mud ball and spread throughout our solar system and beyond. I'm still confident that that is our ultimate fate. In fact, this thought always bolsters my resolve when the pessimists try to prevail," Noah declares.

"Now you have to keep in mind," he continues, "that at this time, almost everyone who could read, listen to a radio or watch television was convinced that the human race was merrily breeding itself into extinction. The only bromide being offered to reverse the trend of ever-accelerating population growth was reproductive restraint—voluntary population control in other words."

"The little book pointed out that restricting reproduction was contra-evolutionary. Biological imperatives and cultural realities are too powerful to be overcome by awareness, education or even government edict. Any meaningful reduction in the world-wide birth rate just wasn't going to happen. Ergo, the population on this planet would continue its meteoric rise."

"I should point out, the author was right. Despite decades of awareness campaigns, government proclamations and the best of intentions, the population of our home planet continues to increase at an ever-more alarming rate. Let me show you how shocking. Please direct your attention to your video monitor once again."

Turning to face your monitor, Noah says in his command voice, "Jason, please display the world-population-growth chart and run the data from AD 1 to AD 2040."

"Yes Noah," a disembodied voice responds.

You look at the chart appearing on your screen. On a blue background, a white horizontal line running the width of the bottom of the display is joined in the lower-right corner by a white vertical line extending to the top of the screen. White index marks are spaced evenly along both lines. The marks on the horizontal line begin with AD 1 on the left and end with AD 2040 on the right. Intermediate indices are spaced evenly between them showing the millennia increasing from left-to-right. The vertical line is similarly equipped. A white "0" is in the lower-right corner and "12 Billion" is to the right of the top of the line. A bold red arc describes the population-growth curve over time.

To your surprise, you note that the red curve starts out at AD1 with a world population of only 200 million people. That's less than the current population of the United States, which reached slightly fewer than 300 million in 2002. The red curve slopes gently upward to the right, reaching 1 billion people around the middle of the 1800s. However, in the early 1900s, the curve slopes upward sharply. A world population of 2 billion is reached by 1930. By 1975, only 45 years later, it has doubled to 4 billion. It rises almost vertically, shooting up to 6 billion by 1999 and 12 billion souls by 2040.

"Can you even imagine living in a world with twice as many people as there are now?" Noah asks. "Well, you won't have to imagine it. I don't know about you, but I plan to be alive in 2040, and we'll be living that overcrowded reality if we don't do something about it."

"In 1978, I was, you see," Noah tells you, "already convinced that the population of this planet was going to go well beyond any reasonable limit. The book only reinforced my thinking. It also bolstered my belief that we had to find a way to start moving significant numbers of humans off the planet. But the questions were, 'how', and 'to where'?"

"Another big factor in my readiness to see my life's mission was the fact that I was searching for meaning in my life. You see, at the time I was firmly established in my chosen profession. As a teenager, I yearned to become an airline pilot and I was lucky enough to reach that goal at the tender age of twenty-one."

"By the time I found the little book, I already had over ten years of seniority with Bravo X-ray Airline and I was looking forward to a rewarding career as a senior airline captain. All I had to do was sit tight, behave myself, do a good job and survive, and I would be able to enjoy a very comfortable lifestyle followed by an equally enjoyable retirement. The only problem was that I was feeling empty and confused."

"With the passage of time, I learned that these feelings were partially an inevitability of my age at the time, and the upheaval going on in the world around me. Strong currents of social change were abroad in the land during this period, and the knowledge that billions of people were living in poverty and hopelessness weighed heavily on my mind. I wanted to do something to help, but what? Fighting hunger and poverty are noble causes, but to my mind, that is only rearranging deck chairs on the Titanic. If we solve these problems—not very likely in my estimation given the evils of greed and fear—we will only exacerbate the problem of over-population."

"At this point in my life, I was financially secure. I had the benefit of almost free travel. My schedule was very flexible and open." "I could," Noah says with a broad smile, "pretty much go anywhere I wanted to go, anytime I wanted to go there and I could afford a wonderful lifestyle at home and on the road. In other words, I had it made. Say, now that I think of it, maybe that was an earlier version of Air Travelers' Heaven. I'll have to look into that, but I'd better get us back on course."

"So there I was," Noah says in a stentorian voice, "in my early thirties, doing what I wanted to do and then some. A great future was stretching before me and I still wasn't happy."

Noah's confession propels you suddenly back in your mind to your own life at that age. You can easily relate to his story. "Maybe his feelings of emptiness and confusion are typical of most humans as they pass through that stage in life," you think.

"I believe you're right," Noah replies to your unspoken observation.

"As anyone who was there will recall," Noah says, "the 1970s were both the most exciting and hopeful, and the most depressing and bleak of times. The Vietnam War, racial strife, the degradation of the environment, the rebellion against the old institutions and customs, the incredible increase in our knowledge base and the light-speed advancement of technology created a heady mix of emotions and ideas in all of us. We must add to that the fact that science was in the early stages of revealing to us that several types of natural disasters could completely annihilate the human race in the blink of an eye, cosmically speaking."

"For example, for the first time, the general public was faced with the fact that, if the scientists were right, an asteroid could strike the earth at any time resulting in the mass extinction of most of the species living on the planet. It turned out that it had happened before, and scientists still believe that it is only a matter of time before it happens again."

"The scientists also cheered us with the news that a killer plague could break out at any time. This could also spell disaster for humankind. And then there was the threat of breakdowns to our food chain due to naturally occurring phenomena or a slip of our own hand through genetic engineering or the use of overly nasty chemicals. Of course, all of this doom and gloom didn't take into account nuclear holocaust or invasion by aliens. The first one everyone knew about, but pretended it wasn't really there. The second one only we science-fiction aficionados believed was possible."

"When everything was taken into account," Noah continues in a subdued voice, "things didn't look too good for the human race in the long run. That was my considered opinion then, and I believe many others held the same view. In fact, the risks haven't abated. If anything, they have become even more threatening and some new ones have been added since then. This one basket is way too dangerous for humankind to keep all its eggs in—literally."

"Please allow me to interrupt," Antoine says with a quick glance in Noah's direction, "for I believe our intrepid air traveler should know one additional tidbit." You and Noah give your attention to Antoine and nod your heads.

Solemnly, Antoine continues, "The most unfortunate aspect of all of this rather dreary future for humankind on earth is the immutable fact that at some point in the future, the star around which earth has been orbiting will explode. When that happens, my friends, all life still living on this planet will be obliterated along with every molecule that makes up the earth. So you see, even if humankind solves all of its life-threatening problems on earth, it will all come to no avail. If humankind remains on only this one planet, it is doomed to extinction."

You stare at Noah and Antoine with a bewildered look. You had not known about this ultimate fate that is in store for humanity. Oh sure, you might have seen a glimpse of something about it on TV as you were surfing through the channels looking for diversionary entertainment. At that time, you certainly didn't think it was anything to worry about.

"Isn't the Sun supposed to stay in one piece for a long time yet?" you ask.

"That depends," says Antoine, "on whom you choose to believe." "Please keep in mind that we have only been studying stars with the proper tools for less than half-a-century now. The people who should know of these things—astrophysicists and cosmologists—believe that it will be four-billion more years before the sun explodes. We hope they are correct, but who knows?"

After a thoughtful pause, you ask, "Do you mean that it's hopeless? That no matter what we do, the human race is doomed?"

"*Au contraire me ami*," Antoine responds. "If humankind can get off this planet and establish viable communities on additional celestial bodies, then there is every chance that we will survive. Of course, we will have to keep moving—out of this solar system, out of this galaxy, maybe even out of this universe. Or should I say out of both your old universe and this one, since they are proceeding along parallel timelines and their physical makeup and laws seem to apply equally to both worlds."

The blinding light of insight fills your mind. "Of course," you say. "*Never again enough people*! If we leave this planet, we'll never again have enough people to overpopulate the environment available to us. Wonderful!" you exclaim. "Instead of facing a future defined by limits and dwindling resources, humankind can forever-more look forward to a universe of truly unlimited wealth and living space. And by spreading out onto different worlds, the threats to the survival of the human race are outflanked. Nothing can get all of us!"

You turn your head to gaze out the cabin window. The sky is still a deep blue with tendrils of cirrus clouds streaking the atmospheric dome high above you. The sun is shining brightly and the air through which you are passing is smooth. Turning back to face your new friends, you say, "Yes! It's all so clear when you explain it that way. I see it. The most important consideration for any living being, including humans, is the survival of the race to which the individual belongs. If the race dies out, then everything that was done before that—*everything*—is meaningless. The individuals within that race, and in fact the race itself, may as well have not existed at all." You sit there stunned at the implications of your epiphany.

Looking Noah squarely in the eyes, you inquire, "So, that's the logic that led you to believe that the survival of the human race was the highest purpose to which you could dedicate your life?"

Noah slowly nods his head, looking at you for signs of understanding.

"Noah, you can count me in. Where do I sign up?" you say.

"Cool your jets, my friend," Noah says. "There'll be time for that later. Right now, please allow me to explain how Air Travelers' Heaven relates to the survival of the human race."

Noah begins by telling you, "When I recognized that the human race would have to leave this planet to ensure its survival, I started thinking about how we were going to do that. Keep in mind that this was just prior to the time that the Space Shuttle started flying."

"Although the path into space had been clearly defined by von Braun and several others, the reality of the early 1980s was that even with the Space Shuttle, we still did not have a transportation system that could take us safely, reliably and affordably from the surface of the earth up to low-earth orbit. The society in your old world still doesn't and probably never will. Here in Air Travelers' Heaven, we are on the verge of acquiring just such a transportation system."

"What do you mean?" you inquire. "Tell me about that next."

"All in due time, my friend, all in due time," Noah rejoins. "Before we get to that, I think it will be instructive for me to tell you a little more of the story so that you can see the linkage between the events I've described so far and the vision the founders had for Air Travelers' Heaven." You eagerly acknowledge your agreement.

You thought the story was interesting before, but this was an exciting new twist. "Imagine," you say, "being able to leave and return to earth in a vehicle that is safe, reliable and affordable—now that's some 'air' traveling that I want to do."

Both Antoine and Noah look at you with a knowing smile. They obviously feel that you are a colleague in the pursuit of real air-travel adventures.

Noah continues, "At the time that my life's mission chose me, I was actively working to focus public attention on the space program and increase the NASA budget. After reading the little book, I re-channeled those efforts into promoting the idea of setting the goal, as humankind's top priority, of creating a transportation system that would allow us to leave, and return to, the planet at will."

"Whenever I appeared on the radio or TV, or when I was interviewed for a magazine or newspaper article, I pushed the idea that humankind needed a revitalized space program to give it the escape hatch it needs to start sending a significant number of people off the planet. I was gratified at the time to discover how many people agreed with me. I thought we were on our way, but the cosmos had a few tricks to throw our way first. I didn't know it then, but it would take another decade before I could really get the ball rolling. You know, sometimes you have to fight a battle more than once to win it."

"By 1980," Noah says, "I had convinced the powers that be at Bravo X-ray Airline to go after the opportunity to take over Space Shuttle operations from NASA after the Space Shuttle completed its orbital-flight-test period. NASA wanted to turn the Shuttle over to private industry so that their funding would be available for the pursuit of new goals like a permanent space station and a Mars mission."

"I wanted Bravo X-ray to take over Space Shuttle operations so that I could fly the darn thing! As a pilot, I couldn't wait to get my hands on that 4.5-million pound, Mach 25 rocketship-glider. Also, I believed that if good old American capitalism were turned loose on space development, things would happen much more quickly."

"Things were going along really well. Bravo X-ray was spending a lot of money pursuing the first of five NASA contracts that would have, by 1985, made it the world's first and only commercial operator of Space Shuttles. Several of my fellow airline pilots and I had formed a professional organization that we used as a vehicle to set up a training academy to transition airline pilots from airline operations to space operations, and to promote our vision of the future of air-and-space transportation. I was planning on flying aboard the Space Shuttle as an observer in 1983. It looked like everything was going to fall into place," Noah says with a definitive gesture of his hand.

"Along about this time," Noah continues, "the last piece of the puzzle fell into my lap. When I discovered it and integrated it into our plan for moving off the planet, I realized that I had the key to making it possible."

"What was the key and how did you find it?" you impatiently ask.

"The key, my friend, is what I call the 'Juan Trippe Trick' and I found it in a book titled *'An American Saga'* that was written by Robert Daily," Noah announces proudly. The look of total confusion on your face prompts him to explain.

"Let me elucidate," Noah begins. "According to Daley, Juan Trippe was born into a family of New York bankers and society heavy weights in the year 1899. He attended Harvard and was planning on entering the family business until he fell in love with flying. As a youth, he had seen some of the very earliest pilots demonstrating the wonders of flight. By 1907, just four years after the Wright Brothers made powered flight a reality, Trippe already had over one-hundred minutes in his pilot's log book—an admirable achievement in a time when flights were measured in minutes-and-seconds."

"I had the good fortune to meet *monsieur* Trippe when he came to Paris in the early 1920s," Antoine interjects. "He wanted to meet all of the French pilots who were active at the time. So, he invited us all to an elaborate *banquet*. We enjoyed ourselves immensely. He was a remarkable businessman and pilot."

Noah picks up the account from there. "That he was. By the late 1920s, Trippe was up to his hips in the nascent U.S. airline industry. He had started an airline, gone bust, started another one and kept on going. Eventually Trippe's vision of a global-air-transportation system was realized in the airline that evolved out of his earlier efforts. That airline was Pan American World Airways. You may have heard of it," Noah quips.

As you nod your head, Noah adjusts the tilt angle on your video monitor and suggests, "If you will direct your attention once again to the screen, I will explain further." You settle back into your seat and give the moving-picture show your entire concentration.

The images appearing on your monitor are of various aircraft flying at low level over a verdant countryside. The first is of a vintage biplane. This sequence is rapidly followed by clips of flying boats, early propeller-driven airliners, four-engine, narrow-body jet transports, jumbo jets and supersonic transports. A scene of the Concorde as it is taking off transforms into an even-more-sleek vehicle with a needle-nose and arrowhead-shaped wings.

The next shot shows the vehicle in a low-earth orbit. The craft is painted in Pan Am livery that is clearly distinguishable as it slowly rotates about its longitudinal axis. It is preparing to dock with a huge, rotating wheel that is obviously a space station. The strains of *"Blue Danube"* are playing in your headset as the vehicle moves majestically towards the safety of the station's docking port.

"2001: A Space Odyssey!" you cry as you suddenly remember the name of the movie from which the last clip was taken.

"Yes," Noah says. "That was Juan Trippe's vision for his company up until the time he passed away. He was also reborn into Air Travelers' Heaven. I can arrange a meeting with him for you if you'd like."

"I'd love that," you say.

"No problem," Noah asserts. "I'll arrange for you to fly with him soon."

"But right now, let me get back to the story," Noah says. "In the span of little more than forty years, Trippe led humanity from the dawn of air transportation—when the best ride you could hope for was a rickety wood-and-fabric biplane—to the threshold of leaving the planet in a sleek airplane-rocketship. You see, that aerospaceplane you saw in the movie is the vehicle that will make it possible for us to leave the planet and come back anytime we want to."

"Of course," you think. "That's what Arthur C. Clarke and Stanley Kubrick were showing us in the movie—a transportation system that could move people safely, routinely and affordably from the surface of the earth to the surface of the moon and back."

"Is the aerospaceplane the 'Juan Trippe Trick' you were talking about Noah?" you ask.

"No," Noah replies. "The aerospaceplane is not the 'Juan Trippe Trick'. The 'Juan Trippe Trick' is what Trippe was going to use to get a fleet of aerospaceplanes built."

Now you are once again confused. "I don't understand," you tell Noah. "Please explain."

"Gladly," he agrees. "You see, Trippe faced a major recurring hurdle throughout his airline-building career—the acquisition of airplanes that fly higher, faster and farther. Since the 1800s, technology had been rapidly advancing, and the technology used in the aviation industry was no exception. Trippe was a pioneer. He was constantly pushing back the frontiers of air travel. To do that, and to enable him to turn a profit while doing so, Trippe came up with a simple tactic that he used over and over again to get the new technology he wanted incorporated into his operation. It is this tactic that we call the 'Juan Trippe Trick'."

Now totally fascinated by Noah's story, you beg him, "Go on. Please go on."

"You see," Noah resumes, "Trippe knew that his competitors were always trying to squeeze the last penny out of their operating budgets. They were constantly trying to avoid putting out hard-earned cash for fancy equipment, even if it did make flying safer, faster and more comfortable. Trippe realized that he would have to lead the way if he was going to get what he wanted—which was generally airplanes that flew higher, faster and farther."

"Trippe always had the best aviation experts he could find on his staff, people like Charles Lindbergh. They were the best of their day. He charged these experts with the responsibility of monitoring the progress of any technology that could be applied to the development of new aviation-related hardware. Whenever a new technological innovation appeared to be about ready for implementation, Trippe and his team would provide whatever boost was needed to get it ready. When it was, Trippe would stand up and announce an order for a batch of airplanes incorporating the new technology."

"His competitors had no choice but to announce that they too would like some of these nifty new flying machines. If they allowed Pan Am to be the only airline to buy them, they would be left in Trippe's dust. In no time at all, the airframers had a full order book and they were off to the races trying to get the new airplanes into the fleets of the world's airlines as quickly as possible."

"That my friend," Noah says with certainty, "is the 'Juan Trippe Trick'. He used emerging technologies as a lever to advance the art and science of air travel. By placing orders for new airplanes incorporating these technologies, he started a feeding frenzy among his competitors that drove the aircraft manufacturers into doing the research, development and design work that was necessary to bring new airplanes to life."

You look at Noah with a growing sense of understanding. "OK," you say. "I can understand how Trippe used his trick to drive aviation progress, but how does that fit in with the Air Travelers' Heaven vision?"

Antoine replies, "You see, do you not, that the Air Travelers' Heaven vision includes moving off this planet? The vision includes using the 'Juan Trippe Trick' to drive the development of the aerospaceplane, for it is this vehicle that will give humankind the ability to freely leave this planet in significant numbers."

"Yes, I can see that now," you reply. "But how specifically is Air Travelers' Heaven using the 'Juan Trippe Trick' to get aerospaceplanes? And while we're at it, where are we going to go when we leave the planet anyway?"

"Those questions are easily answerable," Noah assures you. "Let's start with the 'how' and then move on to the 'where'. But first, there is one thing that you must know. You are well advised to remember it always. It is something that I constantly remind my grandchildren of."

"And what is that, Noah?" you ask.

With a wide grin on his face and a twinkle in his eyes, Noah says, "The meek shall inherit the earth. The rest of us are leaving."

Chapter 8: "Halfway To Anywhere"

"Whether we call it sacrifice, or poetry, or adventure,
it is always the same voice that calls."
                                   Antoine de Saint-Exupéry

"When we came together to form Air Travelers' Heaven in this universe a little more than ten years ago," Noah begins, "the founding citizens were aligned on the vision. They all wanted to set up an operation that would provide a viable alternative to airline travel and they wanted to develop that operation to the point where they could effectively use the 'Juan Trippe Trick' to get aerospaceplanes. Remember, they called this operation Universal Aerospacelines, or UA."

"You see, the founders knew that before any of UA's competitors would take the bait and order their own fleet of aerospaceplanes to fly point-to-point on the earth's surface, UA would have to be a real competitive threat to them. In other words,

UA's order would have to be credible. And to be credible, they believed, UA would have to be flying a fleet of contemporary jets to destinations all over the planet."

"We started out by rounding up a sufficient number of like-minded air travelers. We did this by recruiting them as members in our non-profit organization which was named Air Travelers United, or ATU. ATU spent virtually all of its membership revenues on public-awareness campaigns and political action aimed at improving the aviation infrastructure."

"Many of the folks who became ATU members also wanted to have available to them an alternative to airline travel. This is where UA came in. We launched it by establishing a network of private facilities on airports in the largest cities in the United States. We called these facilities 'AirCenters'. We staffed the AirCenters with partners-operators-customers and based a small fleet of bizjet-type and other general-aviation-type aircraft at each one. These fleets of aircraft fly between the AirCenters, carrying our partners exclusively. Of course, our flights also go to other airports to serve our partners when needed."

"After three years of operations in the U.S., UA established AirCenters in every city in the developed and developing worlds having a population of at least one-million. Appropriate long-range aircraft were acquired and international operations commenced. Two years ago, eight years after UA was established, it had the credibility and financial clout to announce an order for three-hundred aerospaceplanes."

"Along with the order, UA disclosed that it will use these new airplanes to reduce travel times between its international AirCenters. An aerospaceplane can takeoff from, say Dallas, and land in Paris less than one hour later. Obviously, with this vehicle and its established network of AirCenters and fleet of subsonic aircraft, UA will be able to reduce portal-to-portal travel times between any two points on the globe from approximately eighteen hours to around two."

"And just as we anticipated, the 'Juan Trippe Trick' still works. Every major airline on the planet eagerly placed orders for their own fleet of aerospaceplanes. Boeing and Airbus are now working around-the-clock to produce the vehicle."

"Fantastic!" you shout. "It worked! The 'Juan Trippe Trick' actually worked."

"Of course," Noah replies with a Cheshire cat grin on his face. You now believe that he really is the wizard behind the curtain.

"When will the first aerospaceplanes be delivered?" you ask.

"Well," Noah says tentatively, "it usually takes approximately five years to produce a new airplane once the initial orders are placed. Since we placed the first orders two years ago, we would normally expect deliveries to begin in three years. But, we fortunately had the foresight to put into place another plan that would make the time between first-order and first-delivery much shorter."

"What was that plan?" you query.

"Since we were absolutely convinced that an aerospaceplane was possible and that we would be in a position to order a fleet of them within a decade, we created an organization early on to lay the groundwork for its introduction. The time we have to wait after placing the first orders was considerably reduced."

"The organization that accelerated the introduction of the aerospaceplane is known as The Human Trust, or THT. It is a non-profit organization funded by the founders, UA and others who are in alignment with the vision. THT is now one of the most-powerful instruments on the planet for ensuring the survival of the human race."

"The trust has, over the years, funded research and development that greatly reduced the lead-time for the aerospaceplane. It has also spent a considerable amount of time, money and effort to create universal awareness of the aerospaceplane and its implications. THT has also forged a groundswell of support for the introduction of this revolutionary means of transport. That foresight is paying off in shortened delivery times and a ready market for the transportation services the aerospaceplane will provide. We expect the delivery of our first aerospaceplane to take place within the next two years."

"That's great," you observe, "but what about the 'where'? Other than using the aerospaceplane for sub-orbital transportation between cities on the planet, how are you going to use it to leave earth?"

"I'll get to that in a minute," Noah says. "But first let's look at how we used the sub-orbital capabilities of the aerospaceplane to solve a chicken-egg problem that had been plaguing advocates of human emigration since before there were viable spacecraft."

"I came up against this particular chicken-egg problem when I was a high-visibility activist for space development back in the 1980s," Noah explains. "You see, at the time, those of us in the forefront of promoting space development believed strongly that the riches of space provided sufficient economic justification for the development of a space-transportation system that would provide a safe, reliable and affordable means to travel off-and-back-onto this planet. Unfortunately, the bureaucrats held the view that although they agreed that there were treasures in space that could justify the expenditures needed to develop the aerospaceplane, in their minds, the money should not be spent because the value of those riches had not yet been proven."

"We pointed out repeatedly that humankind couldn't explore and settle the new lands, and thereby find and develop the resources, without a safe, reliable and affordable means of traveling to-and-from the new frontier. It was a classic chicken-egg problem. We couldn't get the transportation system that we needed to develop the off-earth resources until we proved that the resources were really valuable enough to justify the development costs of the new transportation system. And we needed to first have the transportation system to obtain the proof."

"This conundrum beleaguered me for years until I finally figured out that we didn't have to justify the aerospaceplane on the basis of space travel. We could justify it because it was the next logical step for very-high-speed, point-to-point travel on earth. This would be relatively easy to do because there are more and more people traveling around the planet all of the time, and the portal-to-portal speed of air travel had been dropping steadily since the deregulation of the airline industry."

"It was simply taking longer and longer to get around the planet. Therefore, we removed the chicken from the puzzle—or maybe it was the egg, I can't remember which—and we were able to make an unassailable case for the aerospaceplane without needing to talk about spaceflight and other far-out ideas. It became a simple case of the public wanting to go higher, faster and farther after decades of plowing through the atmosphere at sub-sonic speeds."

"Please allow me to interrupt," Antoine says, "to explain that the aerospaceplane has the inherent capabilities of flying on-and-off any airliner runway on earth. It can fly between two cities half-a-world away from each other on a sub-orbital trajectory that will require a flight time of approximately one-hour. And it is also able to fly from those airliner runways into low-earth-orbit where it can rendezvous with orbiting space terminals."

"Yes!" you say. "Just like the Pan Am aerospaceplane and the space station in the movie I saw on the monitor."

"That is correct," Antoine says. "The aerospaceplane can fly sub-orbital flight plans and it can also fly into orbit. It is only a matter of—how do you say it—'keeping the pedal to the metal' for a few more minutes and an aerospaceplane will rise from a sub-orbital trajectory into a low-earth orbit."

"And once you're in low-earth orbit, you are at least halfway to anywhere in the solar system," Noah states with authority.

"That doesn't seem right to me," you say as you visualize a picture of the solar system in your mind.

Again reading your thoughts, Noah says, "Please kindly direct your attention to your video monitor while I explain what I mean."

"Now watch this," Noah instructs. "Jason," he commands, "set flight plan for Earth to Mars."

While you are wondering once again who Jason is, your video screen comes alive with an animation of the solar system as if it were seen from directly above the plane of the ecliptic. The Sun is in the center of the screen and the planets are moving in their individual orbits around the sun. There is a bar graph with a single, green bar in the upper-left corner of the display. In the upper-right corner there are two highlighted rectangles, one labeled 'To' and the other 'From'. The word 'Earth' appears in the 'From' rectangle and 'Mars' appears in the 'To' rectangle.

As you stare at the display, Noah says, "Jason is Air Travelers' Heaven's computer system. It performs all of the IT functions that Air Travelers' Heaven needs to keep UA running smoothly. It's a Jocoby, Cohen and Newman, or JCN, 9000 model. It is voice activated, accessible to all of our citizens all of the time from anywhere they may be. We had to give it a name, so we call it 'Jason'. Get it? JCN—Jason."

"Now, pay attention," Noah suggests, "and I'll show you how this works. Jason, launch aerospaceplane on course to rendezvous with space terminal."

You immediately see a red, glowing line rising from the surface of the earth and spiraling out towards a bright blue dot traveling in orbit around the planet. The aerospaceplane's course will obviously rendezvous with the orbiting blue dot at a point considerably down-track from where it is now.

"Now look over here," Noah directs as he points to the bar graph in the upper-left corner of the monitor. As the aerospaceplane travels along its trajectory, the green bar is moving upwards, becoming longer. Two digits followed by a percent sign move with the top of the bar. Noah says, "The green bar shows us the amount of energy that is being expended by the aerospaceplane as it progresses towards its rendezvous point with the space terminal. It is expressed as a percentage of the total energy that must be expended to reach Mars."

"You can see that as the aerospaceplane gets closer and closer to achieving low-earth orbit, the percentage of the energy it takes to get from the surface of the Earth to Mars is going up. Now please take note, our virtual aerospaceplane is now reaching low-earth orbit. As it does, the bar graph is telling us that we have expended approximately fifty-percent of the total energy needed for the entire flight to Mars."

Noah sums up what you have just seen by telling you, "So, as you can easily see, once you achieve low-earth orbit, you are, in terms of energy expended, halfway to anywhere in the solar system. And energy use equates to cost, time and difficulty. The hardest part of space travel has always been, and I suspect it always will be, lifting oneself into a low orbit from the bottom of the huge gravity well created by all large planetary bodies. Once you have achieved low-earth orbit, it becomes relatively easy to escape from the gross effects of a planet's gravity field."

"Jason, activity complete," Noah commands.

"Good day to you Noah and may your takeoffs equal your landings," Jason retorts as it shuts down the video monitor.

It takes a second for Jason's jibe to register in your mind. "Oh great," you say. "Even the computer system likes to joke around."

Noah looks at you with a quizzical gaze and asks, "What joke? My friend, that was a solemn benediction from one aviator to another."

Now you are not sure what to think. Before you have time to sort this out, Antoine interjects, "Noah you must tell our friend where we are going now that you have so ably explained the 'how'."

"You're absolutely right," Noah replies. "We're going to need Jason again. Let me see if I can wake him up."

"Jason, new session please," Noah says in his best command voice.

"Yes Noah, I'm right here. What can I do for you, sir?" Jason responds in his soothing computer-generated voice.

"Activate the video monitor again please and show an interior view of Koch crater," Noah instructs.

The screen lights up with a view that appears to be of a highland valley somewhere on earth. Overhead, a blue sky and rambling white clouds form a dome that looks almost like an earth sky, but not quite.

Your point-of-view is from a scenic overlook high up on the interior wall of a circular ring of low mountains. Their peaks have been sheared off to form an unbroken, flat hoop around the valley. The dome is sealed to the flat ring all around its circumference. The apex of the dome seems to be several thousand feet above your position. You are at least two-thousand feet above the valley floor. It appears to be at least a hundred miles across to the far side of the valley.

Birds flying in the air are joined by humans in strange contraptions strapped to their bodies. The people are using these devices, which have wings and small propellers, to move gracefully through the air. You can see others running along a path next to you. Their strides are much longer than normal. The gravity field in this valley must be much weaker than earth's.

The valley rises uniformly from a large lake in its center to blend with the ramparts of the ring-mountain. You count at least six rivers flowing into the lake from the base of the mountains surrounding the valley. Reservoirs dot the courses of the rivers. The land within the valley is gently rolling with copses, small forests and swaying vegetation blowing in a slight breeze. About one-third of the land in the valley is under cultivation.

Signs of human habitation are scattered about the valley in a seemingly random pattern. The settlements are relatively small. Individual residences, ranches and farms can be seen out in the countryside. You can see several resort-style hotels placed at irregular intervals around the base of the ring-mountain. Some are higher up on the wall.

There are no paved roads in view. Well-kept green pathways, with what look like hovercraft moving briskly along them, can be seen stretching across the valley floor between the villages and towns. Huge gondolas are moving up and down the sides of the ring-mountain on unseen cables. You can barely make out small groups of hikers and bicyclers on the well-defined lanes passing through beautiful forests and over gently rolling plains.

You are in awe. "What can this place be?" you ask.

"You are looking at a computer-created view of the interior of Koch Crater on the moon," Noah informs you. "It is the first crater that we intend to settle when we open up the moon to development. Koch Crater is only the first of what we believe will be thousands of comfortable and safe human communities that will be established in the larger craters all over the moon. This scene shows you how it will look after we dome it over and create an earth-like environment inside. Doesn't it look like a nice place to live?" Noah dreamily asks.

"Wow!" you exclaim. "This has been one wild ride. First I woke up in a new universe after I died in an airplane crash. Then I find out that there's an Air Travelers' Heaven. Next, I find out that the human race is doomed if it stays on earth. After that, I'm told that we're going to shoot around the globe in rocket ships, and now you're showing me that I can routinely travel to-and-from an idyllic valley on the moon. What's next? Is all this possible?"

"The aerospaceplane will make it possible," Noah asserts. "By reducing the cost to lift a pound of payload into orbit by several orders of magnitude, and by making it safe, convenient and comfortable to routinely fly up to low-earth-orbit space stations, it will provide the key to easy access to the rest of the solar system for humankind. Does this sound like the kind of adventure you would like to take part in?"

"Yes, it sure does," you respond. "But now I have a million more questions. The first one is—when is this going to happen? We've all been seeing pretty illustrations of lunar colonies for decades now. Is it sometime in the far-distant future, or is it really just around the corner?"

Noah slides forward in his seat. He places his elbows on his knees and leans toward you. He looks steadily into your eyes. Matter-of-factly, he says, "I plan to be living in a house of my own design in Koch Crater in about ten years."

"Only ten years from now?" you ask.

"Yes, it may even be a little earlier if things go smoothly. We still have to set up the space terminals in low-earth orbit where passengers can transfer from the aerospaceplane to the cislunar shuttle. And we have to build space terminals in lunar orbit so they can transfer from the cislunar shuttle to the lunar landers."

"Of course, we'll be developing Koch Crater in parallel with this work. This plan has been evolving over the past ten years. Just as Air Travelers' United gave us a head start on the aerospaceplane-development project, The Human Trust (THT) made sure we could move quickly to develop the moon once the aerospaceplane is a reality."

"Over the past decade, THT has provided leadership for the large community of human beings who believe that humankinds' destiny lies off this planet. These believers have made contributions of time and money to make sure we have the means to leave the planet and to comfortably settle the moon. And now that deliveries of the aerospaceplane are just around the corner, we've shifted into high gear on the lunar-development project."

You can hardly believe what you are hearing, but you know from what you've heard and how you feel that Noah and Antoine are telling you the truth. Their manner is sincere and what they say makes a lot of sense.

"Noah, I definitely want to live on the moon," you assert. "I've believed for a long time that the type of environment you've shown me, and the relatively low lunar gravity, will extend the life spans of the humans living in such a pleasant locale. Where do I sign up?"

Noah holds up his right hand in the manner of a traffic cop, fingers pointed upward, palm facing you. "Pull your throttle back and drop your flaps, friend," Noah says. "Before you can buy your piece of that particular pie in the sky, you have to qualify. Part of the qualification process is a thorough briefing on the lunar-development plan, the financial commitment you'll have to make, how much money you should earn on the deal and what it's going to be like owning real estate on the moon. If you're truly interested, I'll ask one of the Air Travelers' Heaven citizens who specializes in the deal to walk you through it."

"You 'betcha' Noah," you say in a snappy, confident way. "I'm ready to go!"

As you are about to press Noah and Antoine for more details on the lunar-development project, you hear the two advanced-turbofan engines that power your aircraft smoothly spool down. You are pitched, ever so gently, forward in your seat as the airplane decelerates slightly. You can feel the small reduction in G-force that accompanies the pitch-down of the aircraft's nose and the beginning of a decent.

Antoine, who has been quiet for the past few minutes, leans over you and looks out the cabin window. He straightens up, checks his large, gleaming chronograph, and finally says, "Ah, I see that we are approaching our destination. We should be on the ground in approximately nineteen minutes. *Me Capitan*, is this not your landing?"

Noah stands up, shakes your hand and says, "I'll see you on the ground. After we shut the engines down, why don't you stop by the cockpit for a tour and then we'll take you into the AirCenter and get you oriented?"

"Great!" you reply. "See you then." You can hardly wait. This fantastic flight that you have just enjoyed is, you sense, only the beginning, the tip of the iceberg. You re-check your seatbelt and settle in for the landing and what you are now sure will be an exciting and pleasant experience.

Chapter 9: "Arrival"

"In every crowd...are certain persons
who seem just like the rest,
yet they bear amazing messages."
                    Antoine de Saint-Exupéry
                    "Night Flight"

You and Antoine settle into your individual spaces. You tune your senses into the airplane and the feelings of flight while you look out the cabin window at the arid terrain below. The sun has set and you can see only a few lights scattered across the desert floor like rare, luminescent diamonds. As you get closer to the ground, you pick up enough detail to realize that you are once again on final approach to Runway 26 Right at El Paso International Airport. "Sure enough," you mumble, "there's Fort Bliss."

You turn to Antoine with a bewildered look on your face. The last thing you want is a repeat of the last landing you had here.

He is already looking at you. "Do not worry, *me ami*," he says. "This landing will work out much better than your last. Trust Noah. There is no better pilot in any world. We are completely safe in his capable hands." And with that, Antoine faces forward, closes his eyes and appears to drift off into a serene sleep.

You redirect your attention to the approaching landscape. It is rising up to greet you rapidly now—you must be getting very close to the ground. "How odd," you think. "Just a few minutes ago I was happy and serene in Air Travelers' Heaven. Now my heart is beating like an overworked hydraulic pump and I can actually feel the adrenalin coursing through my veins. I'm afraid! I'm more frightened now than I was on the last landing just before we crashed and I died. I guess it was because before the crash, I was enjoying an acute case of false security. And now I can no longer hide behind casually accepted faulty assumptions that are so easy to believe."

Your panicky thoughts are supercharged by a sudden jolt as a gusty crosswind buffets the airplane—just like the last time! You feel Noah wrestle the airplane back to the runway. The touchdown is once again very smooth. But this time the outcome is quite different. Noah brings the airplane to walking speed with a feather-light touch of the brakes and just the right amount of reverse thrust.

As he turns off the runway and taxies towards the ramp, Noah announces over the PA system, "Fellow citizens of Air Travelers' Heaven, I'd like to welcome you to El Paso, Texas, home of the Diablos. We'll be at the AirCenter in just a couple of minutes and I'd like to take this opportunity to say 'It was nice flying with you again', and please do join me for some welcome-back-to-earth refreshments in the AirCenter lounge after I file my post-flight report. I hope to see you there!"

Noah's invitation has obviously stirred Antoine's interest. He is turning in his seat to look out the cabin window you share and pointing towards something. "Look there my friend," he enthusiastically exclaims. "Do you see the El Paso AirCenter? Is it not *magnifique*?!"

As you focus on the buildings Antoine is pointing at, you come into instant alignment with him—it is beautiful. The main building is three-stories tall, with soaring glass walls enclosing a central atrium. It appears to be about one-hundred-yards in length. You can see people jogging on a balcony running around the perimeter of the roof, and others on the second and third-floor balconies waving to friends who are arriving or departing. A very classy neon sign—or is it really a work of art?—brands the building with the UA logo. The building's architecture has a strong southwest flavor with just the right touch of high tech.

Stretching out to all four points of the compass from the central building are two-story buildings that are about twice as long as the main structure. Each is separated from the main building by a space of at least one football field. A concrete ramp runs around the main building and all four subsidiary structures. The "wings", as they appear to you, are obviously aircraft hangars on the ground level and offices and other facilities on the second level.

Noah turns the airplane to the right to make the turn into the AirCenter ramp. You notice the yellow line with sequentially flashing green lights that he seems to be following is leading into one of the hangars off to the right.

"I see," Antoine remarks, "Noah is following his yellow-brick road to our roosting spot." Sure enough, you see the doors to the hangar you are heading for slide open. Noah taxies the airplane right into the hangar and shuts the engines down. You look back over your right shoulder to see the inside of the hangar and you notice that the hangar doors are gliding into their closed position.

"We're here folks, everybody out of the pool," Noah cheerily announces over the PA system. As your fellow air travelers move leisurely down the aisle towards the open cabin door, each one stops to shake your hand and welcome you to Air Travelers' Heaven. Before resuming their trip down the aisle, each one sincerely offers his or her well wishes for your life in this new world and their hope that you will join them as a citizen.

When the last passenger exits the airplane, Noah steps out of the cockpit and beckons you join him in the front office. As you rise to join him, Antoine stands and extends his hand. Gripping it warmly he says, "It has been my very great pleasure to have met you, *me ami*. I know that we are going to be the very best of friends in the future. It will be my pleasure to sponsor you for an Air Travelers' Heaven citizenship when you are ready; but for now I must take my leave. You see, I have reserved a bizjet that I will personally pilot from here to Puerto Vallarta, Mexico where I intend to spend the weekend matching wits with very-large and very-aggressive monsters of the deep."

"Until we meet again my friend," Antoine intones, "please allow me to leave you with this consideration. As we were landing a few minutes ago, I was of course hearing your thoughts. You are absolutely right about the issue of false security versus real security."

"You see, I believe that false security is just as good as real security, as long as it is not put to the test. False security can make us feel just as safe as real security does. However, when false security is tested, and trust me, it inevitably is, it proves to be insufficient. It will not provide one with the essential things such as a long life and the avoidance of serious injury." Antoine smiles, pivots on his left heel and strides to the exit. And with a wave of his hand, he offers a cheery *"Bon jour, me ami."*

You remain in your seat for a minute, considering Antoine's little speech. As you rise to move forward to the cockpit, you tell yourself, "I will never again fool myself with false security. Look how much it cost me the last time I did. I lost my family, my world and even my life. Never again," you mutter.

With thoughts of your lost loved ones running through your mind and tears welling up in your eyes, you tentatively shuffle towards the open cockpit door. As you approach, Noah jumps up from the left-cockpit seat, slides past you and gestures for you to take it. Before you can take him up on the offer though, he puts his hand on your shoulder, looks into your eyes and says, "Don't be sad about your losses. There is nothing you can do about it now. I know it's hard, but it will get easier with time. You'll find that you will be welcomed here in Air Travelers' Heaven and everything will work out in the end. Now, I suggest that you keep your attention on the briefings we are giving you so that you can start that adjustment as soon as possible."

You acknowledge Noah with a nod and insert yourself into the vacated captain's seat. When you have settled in, Noah says, "Let me introduce you to my copilot on this flight, Captain Toni Pilot. Toni will give you your briefing on our airplane and then bring you along to the AirCenter's lounge where we'll join up again. I'll see you there. I have to go file my reports."

✈

As Noah turns to leave, you look at the woman sitting in the copilot's seat. She appears to be in her early thirties. Her golden hair is cut short in a very professional style. Her blue eyes seem to look right through you and welcome you at the same time. The smile on her face and in her eyes puts you immediately at ease. You notice that her eyes also have barely noticable crows-feet emanating from their corners.

Captain Pilot speaks first. "Hi, I'm Toni," she says as she offers you her hand in greeting. "Noah told me that you're a new arrival—welcome. I picked up your thoughts about your family as you came towards the cockpit. I know how you feel. I just got here a few months ago myself. Thank God it's Air Travelers' Heaven, and not Hell. I died in an airline crash just like you, only it was my fault."

"You see, I insisted on continuing to fly my regular schedule back in our other world even though I was going through a nasty divorce at the time. That, and an overly long duty day that I was trying to survive while suffering from a cold, were the final links in the error chain that led to my demise; and unfortunately the death of many others. So, not only do I miss my loved ones, but I also still carry the guilt of screwing up so badly that—by my own hand—I caused so much anguish for so many people."

You can see clearly that Toni is sincere. The telling of her story also forges a bond between the two of you. Amazingly, your feelings of emptiness seem a little more tolerable now that you know that you are not alone in your misery. Gazing steadily into Toni's eyes, you tell her, "Thank you for sharing that with me. It does make me feel a little better."

With a warm feeling of camaraderie, you both turn your attention back to the cockpit. Toni begins your briefing, "As you can see, we have five twelve-inch by fourteen-inch, flat-panel, liquid-crystal displays mounted in our forward instrument panel. These displays give us all the information we could possibly need, and then some—about where we are, where we're going, what it looks like up ahead and the operation of the airplane's systems. I can assure you that this is the very latest guidance, navigation and control technology available."

"Does UA put that kind of technology into all its airplanes?" you ask.

"It sure does," Toni answers. "In fact, part of the founders' vision back at the beginning was their belief that they could improve the safety of flying in a passenger jet at least fifty-percent by installing the latest, proven safety-enhancing technologies. As it's turned out, the actual safety benefit has been much higher."

"Here's a good example," Toni says as she points to a trapezoidal pane of glass, about eight-inches across, mounted at eye-level between your head and the windshield. "Look through the glass—it's called a head-up display, or HUD—and you'll see what I mean." You sit squarely in the captain's seat and peer out through the HUD. You can clearly see the hangar wall about fifty-feet away. Superimposed on the glass pane are brightly lit blue-green symbols.

"This is just like the displays fighter pilots use in their combat jets," you state. "I've seen it on CNN a hundred times."

"That's almost right," Toni says. "In our old world, jet fighters did in fact use head-up displays similar to this one. But we have an innovation that goes those fighter jocks one better."

"Just give me a second to put the system into simulator mode, and I'll show you what I mean," Toni says. Opening the cockpit's side window, she calls out, "Hey Pete, I'm going to run a short avionics simulation. Will you please douse the hangar lights for a few minutes?"

After receiving a thumbs-up from Pete, Toni reaches down and starts diddling with a computer-interface unit's keyboard. You continue to look through the HUD. As the hangar lights go down, you see something new projected onto the glass plate. It's a black-and-white, negative-view picture of a runway seen from about five miles out on final approach.

"What you're looking at there, is a replay of our approach to Runway 26 Right here in El Paso a few minutes ago," Toni tells you. "As you can see, although the image is reversed as in a photo negative, you can clearly make out the runway, the taxiways, the ramps and the buildings on the airport. You'd see that same picture even if you were trying to look through clouds extending all the way down to the runway. It's done with infra-red sensors, global-positioning satellite receivers and a lot of computing power. It's called an enhanced-vision system or E-V-S."

Toni flashes some kind of coded message to Pete with her pocket flashlight and the hangar lights come back up. "In my opinion," Toni offers, "this one innovation alone enhances flight safety by at least fifty-percent. It makes a dark-hole approach a piece of cake. It also takes the sweat out of low-visibility landings. If you would have had one of these systems aboard the airplane you crashed in, you probably wouldn't have crashed! But the truly sad fact is that these EVS systems were available to the airline you were entrusting your life to. They just didn't want to spend the money and the FAA wouldn't make them do it. But we put them in all of our jets."

Toni's words cause you to momentarily lose your breath! You feel as if you have just been punched in the stomach. "Are you telling me that these systems were available to the airline, but they wouldn't spend the time or money to install them?" you ask.

"Yes," Toni replies. "The bottom-line drives everything that the airline managers do or don't do."

You feel your anger begin to rise. "Why those cheap, bottom-line-driven bastards," you blurt out. "I could have been safely at home with my family right now if they hadn't skimped on safety equipment like this EVS."

Toni reaches over and places her arm around your shoulder. "Hold on now. Getting angry isn't going to do any good," she says. "We can't change the past, no one can; but we can change the future. That's why Air Travelers' Heaven came into being. We believe that the application of improvements in information technology and human factors can make air travel safer and more enjoyable than ever before. And making air travel safer and more enjoyable is our commitment to our citizens."

As you begin to calm down, you realize Toni is right. You can't change the past, but you can help shape the future. Now more than ever, you want to hear and see the rest of the Air Travelers' Heaven story. You ask Toni to continue.

"There're many other technological innovations I could tell you about that are part of this jet, and all of the other airplanes in Air Travelers' Heaven, but I think we should hurry along to meet up with Noah. I'd guess he's probably just about done with his post-flight debriefing by now. Do you have any specific questions that I can answer for you right now?"

"No," you say. "No specific questions, just a million general ones. But, I can see now what you mean when you say the Air Travelers' Heaven vision was to improve the safety of flight for its citizens by at least fifty-percent and that it has succeeded admirably."

"That's right," Toni says, "and I'll be happy to answer your other questions later. For now though, we'd better catch up with Noah. If we give him too much of a head start, he'll have captured all the hors d'oeuvres and interesting conversationalists by the time we get there."

You extricate yourselves from the cockpit and leave the airplane. As you stroll across the hangar floor, Toni says to you, "You know, UA does a lot of other things that airlines don't do to ensure the highest level of safety. And since the crash you died in was contributed to by pilot impairment, I probably should mention a few of them. I'll brief you when we get to the people mover."

While you are trying to figure out what a people mover is, Toni leads you down a short flight of stairs that runs below the hangar door. At the bottom is a rubber-wheeled carriage that resembles a large, clear-plastic bubble mating with a golf cart. "Jump in," Toni suggests. "This is the people mover. It'll take us over to the AirCenter lobby. We can talk on the way."

As soon as you take your seat, the carriage starts slowly moving along a concrete roadway that is traveling through a tunnel. Attractively signed passenger stops offer access to the other hangars and the facilities located above them.

"This people mover is really slick," Toni says. "They're installed in all of our AirCenters. They're computer controlled and electrically propelled, and they keep us out of the weather as we travel to-and-from our departing and arriving aircraft."

"Just like Disney World," you say.

Toni resumes her briefing by telling you that UA's pilots are restricted to a ten-hour duty day with no more than six hours of actual flight time during that period. She also points out that the pilots must have at least twelve hours off between duty periods, and they fly no more than three days a week. Their schedules are arranged so that they are home almost every night, and they have plenty of schedule flexibility to allow for life's surprises and their own biorhythms.

"We are encouraged," she tells you, "to ground ourselves if we do not feel one-hundred-percent like flying. And we're rewarded for making the right decision. The most important thing, though, is that every UA pilot is screened for impairment before, and during every flight. And we're required to spend at least two hours a week with other pilots or other citizens in frank, one-on-one and group discussions. We talk about ourselves and what's going on in our lives."

In summation Toni tells you, "It all may sound kind of 1984-ish, but it really is no imposition if you understand the why and how. The why is because every living pilot has an excellent appreciation for her or his personal limitations and the adverse effects impairment can have on them. We want to, more than anyone else, and before every takeoff and landing, know objectively just how much we are impaired."

"We check our level of impairment with a simple program running on a personal-digital-assistant platform. Just like the one I'm sure you have your personal schedule and telephone book on. Here, take a look at mine. I'll show you how this works."

Toni pulls her PDA out of her uniform-shirt pocket and turns it on. She begins the demonstration by saying, "The program presents several simple displays. Most of them are grid patterns or moving targets. I have to accurately respond to the challenges that are presented in a timely manner. See how it works?"

Toni goes through the various short tests the PDA is offering up and says, "There. That's it. I've completed the impairment test. Now, I'll hit the 'Tell Me' icon and we'll have the results in about two seconds."

"You see," Toni continues, "my responses are recorded, compared to two databases—my personal history and all UA pilots—sifted through a filter and tortured by an algorithm to produce my impairment, or 'I', reading. Here's mine coming up now. It says my I-reading is 'nine'. That's pretty good. The high end of the scale is 'ten', which translates into a reading of no impairment. If it goes below 'eight', I start to be a little more careful. If it is less than 'six', I ground myself. We'll, what do you think?"

"That sure is impressive," you respond. "I wish the pilots in my old universe had used one of those. I might still be alive over there. I'll tell you one thing though, if I used that thing before every game of golf that I play for money, I'm sure I can cut my losses."

Toni smiles and says, "You know, you can be impaired by many things in addition to alcohol and drugs. Stress, fatigue and distraction can cause a higher level of impairment than either one of those, and they take far more lives in aviation mishaps. That's why we check for any level of impairment while the pilot is on duty, not just a urine test every so often."

"And the meetings with our fellow Air Travelers' Heaven citizens, well those are actually fun. We enjoy each others' company and help each other out with a lot of things. And we all know that we are aligned with the idea that we want to keep each other well. So, we agreed that we are each required by the rules that we have all settled on to help each other with any problems that might arise. We have found that this process virtually eliminates the possibility that a pilot bent on suicide will be allowed to fly a UA airplane."

To put it mildly, you are stunned by what you are hearing. How can this be? Pilots who are required to open up to their coworkers and fellow citizens and computer-based tests for impairment? It all makes sense. "How come the airlines of my world didn't do this?" you ask.

"That answer is easy," Toni answers. "M-O-N-E-Y—the good old bottom line. You see, if you test pilots for impairment and find that they are impaired beyond a reasonable limit, you can't, in good conscience, let those pilots fly, even if they want to and you really need them to. If you send them home until they're ready to fly, you have to have another pilot standing by to take their place, and that, I'm afraid, costs money."

"In your old world, the bureaucrats running the airline system could sidestep the issue of impairment by mandating an infrequent drug test. This is merely eyewash, something to lead the public to think that the airlines are really taking care of them. All the while, these highly effective and easily available impairment-testing devices are kept hidden in the closet even though they have been around since the early 1980s. Once again, the bean counters made the decision, without input from you, or any real concern for your well-being, to forgo increased safety to facilitate the lining of their own pockets. If that's not a case of false security on the part of their passengers, I've never seen one."

"On the other hand, the Air Travelers' Heaven citizens are all owners, customers and operators of their air-travel system. Therefore, we can balance the trade-offs between economics and safety from a different perspective than the airline bureaucrats—from inside our own skins. But you know what? Even when we take into account the costs of these new bells and whistles that make us safer, the overall cost of air travel for the citizens is still lower than the airfares that they would have to pay to the airlines."

"I believe you," you tell Toni . "It all makes sense to me. What were those airline lunkheads thinking?"

"That's another easy question," Toni says. "They were thinking about their stock options and their golden parachutes."

As your people-mover carriage approaches the stop for the main lobby, Toni offers one more insight. "Another safety-enhancing strategy that UA embraced, from the very beginning, is their policy of hiring only very senior pilots to act as pilot-in-command aboard all their jets."

"You see," she continues, "if a pilot is flying for an airline, he or she is forced to retire at the age of sixty. Now, for some pilots, that's probably a good idea, but for the vast majority, that's like telling a top-notch surgeon, lawyer or business person that sixty is the end of the road. Good bye. You are no longer useful."

"In my humble opinion," Toni inserts, "just because you've reached an arbitrarily placed milestone on the road of life, there is no reason to believe that you are no longer fit to practice your life's work. The founders of Air Travelers' Heaven believed, and I couldn't agree more, that forcing pilots to retire at age sixty is not only stupid, it is very wasteful."

"So they found a way to tap into that valuable resource. We're grateful for the airlines' short sightedness. We get all the skilled, well-trained and talented pilots we need from the ranks of retiring airline pilots. And they can fly with us because under the FAA rules that regulate us, they may continue to fly until they can no longer pass their physicals. Of course, they are closely monitored to make sure their cognitive and motor-skill performance is first-rate."

"What about the copilots?" you ask, stepping from the halted carriage.

"Universal Aerospacelines recruits all of its copilots while they're still in high school," Toni explains. "Air Travelers United has established an aviation club in every high school in North America. These aviation clubs supply more than enough budding young pilots to our UA Flight Academy."

"Once they enter the academy, it only takes about two years to get them fully qualified to fly as copilots. They even get their bachelor degrees during that time. UA's system of selecting, training and seasoning pilots is world-renowned. In fact, we are the major supplier of new-hire pilots to all the airlines. After they fly for us for two years, we push our young birds out of the nest to go fly for the other airlines until they are forced to retire at sixty. Then we hire them back as senior captains and mentors for the emerging aviators coming up through the system."

"Pretty slick," you remark.

"Yes it is," Toni says. "And it's profitable too. The UA Flight Academy is a nice profit center within the UA umbrella. The UA Academy also trains all of our citizens who pilot, for their own pleasure and personal-transportation needs, general-aviation aircraft. Of course, the academy is also responsible for all the initial and recurrent training that is needed by our line pilots. All-in-all, the UA Flight Academy is an integral part of our success and it is vital to our enhanced-safety program."

"UA also has a policy of pairing only senior captains with up-and-coming copilots. That has proven to be the optimum blend of experience to enhance safety. And it also creates an environment that is conducive to passing along the wisdom of the masters to future generations of UA captains."

"Let me give you one last word on pilots and superior safety," Toni continues. "UA flies all of its jets with three pilots aboard whenever the configuration of the airplane allows for it. This has been proven to enhance safety and it also trains new pilots who are just beginning their professional-piloting careers. The third pilot is an extra pair of eyes, ears and hands that reduce a lot of the workload for the captain and first officer in normal and stressful situations. And what better way is there for a new pilot to earn his or her wings than to study with the masters?"

Chapter 10: "Real Security"

"He's right, he is, the captain."
                    Antoine de Saint-Exupéry
                    "Flight To Arras"

As you and Toni exit the people mover, she ends her briefing on UA pilots. Pointing up the broad ramp in front of you, she says, "After you, please." Your gaze follows her outstretched arm and you find yourself looking up into an atrium that is three-stories high. The tram stop is obviously one floor below and just outside the ground floor of the atrium, so you are actually looking up four stories. It is very impressive. On the interior side of the atrium, you can see tiered balconies, vegetation, neon signage and a huge UA logo tastefully arranged so as to create a very pleasing environment.

Toni notices that you are staring at the interior of the building with a look of wonderment on your face. She says, "UA's image was created by a design genius who was one of its founders. He's a marketing guru who also branded UA and produced all of its promotional materials. You'll probably run into him on a UA flight. He travels all over the world consulting to some of the largest organizations on the planet."

As you walk up the ramp and arrive at the ground-floor lobby, you take in the sights. One side of the lobby is devoted to a security-screening checkpoint with a large, comfortable lounge area. There seem to be less than fifty people sitting quietly or talking in small groups. On the far side of the lounge, you can see a sign with an arrow pointing down. The sign says "Departing Flights". It must be another ramp leading down to the people mover.

Toni interrupts your surveillance by saying, "Not only do all of the citizens traveling on our airplanes have extensive background checks completed on them by UA security, but every single bag that gets past that security checkpoint will have been thoroughly checked for explosives, weapons and other dangerous articles."

You marvel at the tight security and the lack of lines and confusion at the security checkpoint. Toni explains this by telling you, "The background checks, the retinal scans at the entrance and the personal-identification smartcard carried by all citizens make each AirCenter virtually a gated enclave for our air travelers."

"By keeping our individual passenger loads down to a reasonable number, and by using these advanced security techniques, we have eliminated the time-consuming, frustrating, intimidating, costly and sometimes-embarrassing security that is still used by the airlines today. All of our passengers feel much more secure with us than they do when flying on the airlines—because they are."

You turn your attention to the other side of the lobby. Behind a two-story glass wall, you can see four aircraft simulators moving up-and-down and side-to-side on long, spindly legs.

Reading your thoughts, Toni explains, "We have a UA Flight Academy operation in each of our AirCenters. You're looking at simulators for the four types of jet aircraft we are currently operating. Our pilots use them for training, and all of our citizens have access to them for orientation simulations and just plain fun. Later we can go over to the academy area and you can see how we use the latest technologies to train our new pilots and support those who have learned to fly with us earlier."

"But right now," Toni says, "please step over here with me." Both of you walk leisurely over to one end of the lobby where a huge, circular conversation pit is located. As you and Toni step down into the depressed area, you can clearly see a large holographic display perched atop a central pedestal. It appears to be a three-dimensional, full-color hologram of the AirCenter complex.

"If you don't mind," Toni says, "we can use this AirCenter hologram to take a virtual tour of the complex." As you stare at the incredibly life-like image of the AirCenter, Toni steps over and begins to manipulate a touch-screen. "Now," she starts, "please pay attention to the highlighted areas as I take you on the tour." You sit down on the comfortable couch and give Toni your full attention.

"We are now in the central, main building of the complex," Toni says. You can see two human-like figures standing in the virtual lobby. They must represent you and Toni.

"If you'll look right here," Toni says as you follow the little red dot being emitted from the end of her laser pointer, "you can see the lobby we are in, the UA departure lounge, the simulator bay, the Air Travelers United Store, and The Human Trust Learning Center. As you can see, they are all located on the first floor."

The image changes and Toni continues, "Now, here's the basement below us. It houses all of the mechanical equipment for the building and emergency shelters in case they're needed. Let's move on to the second floor."

The new image reveals the floor above you. "On this floor," Toni points out, "we have offices and meeting rooms that our partners can use when they are transiting the AirCenter. There are also office suites that some of our local citizens lease for conducting their business. They like to be close to their airplanes. This floor also has a few hotel rooms in case a citizen needs to take a short rest while enroute from one AirCenter to another. It also has office space that is devoted to our local-administration team."

"The third floor houses our local operations center, or 'OpsCenter' as we call it. Let's take a closer look at that." The image of the OpsCenter enlarges until it is the only thing displayed on the pedestal. Now you can see that this is a real-time, live look at the OpsCenter located two stories above your head. The area you are looking at is one large room. The wrap-around, floor-to-ceiling windows give the occupants of the OpsCenter a panoramic view of the AirCenter complex, the airport and the surrounding environment.

You can see a centralized bank of large-screen displays located along the center of the room. There are three tiers of computer work stations arrayed around the central displays. At least fifty people are occupying the work stations. They are either talking on the telephone or pecking away at a keyboard. It looks a lot like Mission Control.

"This local OpsCenter is responsible for supporting all of the citizens living within the market area this AirCenter is serving. Its primary function is to support UA flight operations. But it also provides active flight following, instant communications, executive travel-agent services and many other support services to our citizens."

"In other words, it is the nerve center for all UA operations in this area. Of course, it's tied in with OpsCenter Central and all the other OpsCenters to form a support network that is in constant communication with our citizens and assets."

"And Jason is the backbone of the whole operation. I understand that you've already met him," Toni says.

"Yes I have," you reply. "He's quite an impressive fellow."

"He is that," Toni says. "A system like Jason is a rarity. As Noah probably told you, Air Travelers' Heaven spent a lot of time and money in the beginning to get him up-and-running. But it's been well worth it."

"Let me give you a demonstration of how the system works," Toni says as she pulls her PDA out of her pocket once again. "This little beauty," she begins, "is also my Air Travelers' Heaven Communicator—or A-T-H-C as we call it. Every citizen has one. It operates like a typical PDA, but it has several enhancements that make it unique. First of all, it has a built-in GPS receiver, so it always knows where it is. Secondly, it has a wireless connection to Jason."

"Now take a look at this," Toni suggests. You move next to her so you can see the full-color display on the PDA. Toni says, "Watch this," as she touches her finger to the UA icon in the center of the screen. An icon-based menu appears with several selections. Toni touches the "Find-Me" icon. With no noticeable delay, a message appears telling you that you are presently located in the El Paso AirCenter. "OK," Toni says, "now that we know where we are, I'll touch the 'Where-To?' icon, which is represented by this bulls eye, and presto!"

A "Define-Destination" prompt appears. "Now all I have to do is tell Jason where I want to go, and we can start getting some answers," she says. Toni then intones into the PDA's built-in microphone, "Home AirCenter."

The ensuing dialogue between Toni and Jason yields a choice of times and methods whereby Toni can get from where she's at to where she's going. "All I have to do now," Toni explains, "is make a decision about when I want to leave and get there, and by what means—a chartered jet, a single seat on a UA flight, or even a seat on an airliner—and Jason will take care of everything, even the ground transportation and any hotel rooms I may need. In fact, the combination of my ATHC, Jason and the people staffing the OpsCenter can solve any transportation-related problem I can throw at them. Pretty neat, huh?" Toni asks. You nod your head in agreement, awed by this quantum leap in air-traveler support.

"Before we leave the OpsCenter, there's one more aspect I'd like to point out," Toni continues. "The OpsCenter is also responsible for dispatching all of our aircraft. UA uses the same procedure that's used by the airlines for dispatching their flights. Both the captain of the flight and an FAA-certified UA dispatcher must agree on the particulars of each flight before it is released. There's nothing unusual there, if you're applying the highest-available safety standards to your flight operation. The twist comes in with the fact that UA also dispatches all of its private flights—those flown by pilot-citizens themselves—under the same rules."

Slightly confused, you ask, "And why is that Toni?"

"That is because," Toni replies, "my non-pilot friend, most of the private pilots who manage to get into fatal trouble do so because they don't have the benefit of a professional-level dispatch system. Poor and inexperienced judgment is the biggest killer of general-aviation pilots."

"We support our pilot-citizens who fly private aircraft with an airline-level dispatch operation. They never have to make a critical decision on their own. They always have the ability to—in fact they are required to—avail themselves of the expertise obtainable from UA aviation veterans before making a decision to begin or continue a flight. And if they are away from home and the return flight is beyond their capabilities or that of the airplane they are flying, UA provides free transportation for the pilot-citizen and his or her passengers. This ensures that the pressure to get home doesn't push one of our citizens into a tragic mistake."

"And speaking of safety," Toni says, "there is one other aspect I should touch on if you're thinking of learning to fly. Are you?"

"Well, yes," you tentatively reply. "I've always wanted to learn to fly, but I never had the time or money to pursue it."

"No problem," Toni asserts. "Here in Air Travelers' Heaven, you'll find that available time to chase your dreams and enough money to do what you want are not a big concern. You may not know it, but just about one person out of two has a desire to learn to fly. The UA Flight Academy has the right flight-training program for anyone who has been harboring a secret dream of becoming a pilot. UA Flight Academy's training programs are the safest and most effective that have ever been devised. That's why they produce the safest pilots."

"You know," you say, "that's been one of my biggest concerns about learning to fly—the safety factor."

"I know what you mean," Toni testifies. "Pilots are the type to seek challenge and adventure, but here in Air Travelers' Heaven we want them to be as safe as possible while doing it. Most flight-training programs focus on graduating the student in as short a time as possible. Those flight schools are only concerned with training the student to minimum government standards."

"The UA Flight Academy takes the time to train its student pilots to standards that are much higher. It uses the best available training technology to get the job done. The fact that the Academy uses all new airplanes equipped with the latest technological innovations for its training and aircraft-rental programs also greatly enhances the safety level of the operation. Most flight schools are still using thirty-year-old airplanes in their training and rental fleets."

Looking at her watch, Toni comments, "We better move this briefing along if we want to rendezvous with Noah in the lounge. Let's take a quick look at the roof of this building and one other thing and then we can join up with him." You focus your attention on the hologram as it transforms itself into a view of the roof of the building you are in.

"As you can see," Toni goes on, "the roof of the central building is devoted to our citizens' health and relaxation." An Olympic-size swimming pool is recessed into the roof. A large, glass-enclosed area housing a well-equipped workout space is located at one end of the building. Several people are working out on the Stairmasters, treadmills, stationary bicycles and Bowflex machines enclosed by the glass dome. Couples and small groups are lounging around the pool, engaged in casual conversation and relaxing drinks. A few people are jogging around the track that is installed on the balcony running around the perimeter of the roof. These must be the folks you saw earlier.

"This fitness center is available to our local citizens and their guests and to any citizen passing through the AirCenter," Toni informs you. "The fitness centers have proven to be instrumental in improving our citizens' health and in providing them with a tranquil social opportunity."

"The last thing that I would like to show you is one of the outlying buildings in the complex," Toni says as she changes the hologram to show the building your airplane parked in. "As you can see here on the ground floor, we have hangars with doors on two sides so that the aircraft can taxi in and taxi out. This saves a lot of time and a lot of money that would have to be spent on ground crews and their equipment. It also keeps our partners out of the elements when they are boarding a flight."

"What a clever idea," you say.

"On the second floor, you can see that we have plenty of room for our local UA Flight Academy, staff areas and additional office space," Toni concludes. "If you'll follow me," Toni requests, "we'll move along to the Control Tower Lounge to meet up with Noah and the entourage I'm sure he's collected by now."

You follow her along a central corridor to one end of the main building. You reach the end of the corridor and step out into a triangular space that appears to be at least one-hundred feet on each side. Its glass walls soar over four stories above you. It is a huge glass prism set on end. Access to the upper floors is provided by a glass-enclosed elevator and a spiral staircase.

"Come on," Toni beckons. "Let's get some exercise." She bounds up the first flight of stairs.

When you reach the second floor, you pause for breath while Toni acts as the tour guide. "Look there, back into the second floor of the main building," Toni says as she points to a glass wall that is fifty-feet away. Beyond the glass wall, you see the kitchen staff busily preparing meals and snacks. "That's the kitchen for the AirCenter restaurant. It also supplies the catering for UA flights. The food is always excellent and reasonably priced, and we know for sure that it's clean and that only the best is served."

The mention and sight of food suddenly set off pangs of hunger in your stomach. You remember that the last thing you had to eat was that airline-terminal sandwich that you bought in Dallas. "When was that?" you wonder. "Was it just a few hours ago? Or was that a few days ago now? What world was I in then, anyhow? What difference does it make anyway—I'M HUNGRY."

Just as the aroma of gourmet food is about to put you over the edge, Toni breaks in, "Hang on a little longer, 'pardner', you can bet we'll find plenty to eat when we locate Noah."

As you continue to ascend the spiral staircase, you notice that the third floor of the glass prism is a large dining area. The patrons who occupy most of the tables and booths have a two-hundred-seventy-degree view of the airport and surrounding environs. Each diner is provided with a TV monitor recessed into the table top. Toni stops briefly to wave at someone she knows and you take this opportunity to more closely inspect the room.

Noticing your curiosity, Toni says, "This is the main dining area. Citizens and their guests can enjoy a gourmet meal or a light snack here." Your eyes roam over the delicious-looking meals being hovered over by happy-looking people.

"Those TVs you see in front of each of them are an interactive portal to Air Travelers' Heaven. By merely pressing the appropriate icons on the touch-sensitive screen, you can access over two-hundred channels. They can provide you with flight and weather information, a profile of your flight crew, live images from inside any of our training airplanes that may be flying right now, infomercials that will explain any aspect of Air Travelers' Heaven that you may be interested in, and much, much more. You can also use the device to communicate with the OpsCenter to book a seat or schedule a flying lesson, place your dinner order or discreetly network with anyone else in the room or aboard a UA flight. Come on now, we have only one more flight of stairs and then we should have Noah cornered."

As you emerge from the staircase on the fourth floor and into the Control Tower Lounge, you are greeted by an aviation-inspired ambiance, one that has been heavily influenced by the set up found in an air-traffic-control tower. You have a three-hundred-sixty-degree view through the floor-to-ceiling windows surrounding the room. There is a large, circular-shaped bar in the center of the room with TV monitors set into the bar's top. Real surveillance-radar displays are hanging from the ceiling over the bar. The eerily glowing blips that represent aircraft in flight crawl slowly across the screens. Very-soothing music floats through the room. It's Frank Sinatra singing *"Fly Me To The Moon"*.

The light is subdued and there is a muted background hum of cheerful voices engaged in lively conversation. Most of the tables and booths are occupied. The room is crowded, but the feeling is one of camaraderie and good will. A hint of lime is in the air and you can smell the delicious scent of cooking. Your hunger pangs return with a vengeance.

Toni grabs your elbow and directs you towards one corner of the room. As you walk around the bar, you see Noah seated at a table located in the corner. There are three people with him. He immediately spots you and beckons you over.

Everyone at the table rearranges the seating plan to make room for you next to Noah. As you take your seat, Noah announces to the table, "For those of you who don't know, this is our new arrival." With that, there is a round of applause and good wishes. You immediately feel at ease. You are obviously among fellow air-travel enthusiasts. The joviality abates and everyone seems to be looking at you with a sense of expectation.

As you stare back with a blank look on your face, Noah says, "Well, did Captain Pilot give you the nickel tour?"

"Yes," you reply, "she sure did and I think I understand things a lot better now."

"Well then, why don't you tell us what you've learned so far?" Noah suggests. At first you think he is kidding you again, but the look on his face tells you that he wants you to tell him what you think you know so that he can make sure that you truly have 'gotten it' so far.

"Well," you tentatively begin, "I understand that I died in that airplane crash and that I somehow came back to life here in Air Travelers' Heaven. I can see why you call it Air Travelers' Heaven, what with all the innovations UA has provided for dyed-in-the-wool air-travelers. I like the set up and I sincerely want to become a citizen of Air Travelers' Heaven if you'll have me."

"I think I'm going to need a little more time to fully understand the vision of creating a gateway for humankind to start moving off this planet, but at this point I have to say that I agree with the idea. And if creating that gateway includes providing me with aerospaceplanes that can fly me halfway around the world in an hour, then what have I got to lose? I'm totally sold on the vast increase in safety, security and convenience that you have built into Air Travelers' Heaven. I'm in, if you'll have me."

Noah's broad smile tells you that you have pleased him. The others at the table are also looking at you with an air of acceptance. You feel at home. Seemingly out of nowhere, a waiter appears at your side with a tray holding a large salad bowl and a huge platter. He arranges them in front of you and informs you that as soon as you are ready for it, he will bring your dessert. You are starting to get more comfortable with the idea of people reading your mind. It obviously can be very convenient—in some cases.

The food looks tasty. You start with the salad. It is a spinach salad with an incredible raspberry-vinaigrette dressing. Your entrée is grilled Alaskan salmon with roasted vegetables on the side. There is also a generous portion of wild rice pilaf gracing the platter. You tuck into your meal with relish. It's delicious.

"While you're enjoying your dinner—by the way, the salmon was flown in from Fairbanks about two hours ago—let me introduce some of my fellow citizens," Noah jovially suggests. "The lovely lady sitting across from me is Stephanie; she's a marine biologist and pilot. As you can see, she's drinking mineral water because she plans to fly a group of her colleagues down to Guaymas this evening in one of our bizjets. They're planning to board a research vessel there for a little cruise in the *Golfo de California.*" Stephanie gives you a warm smile and a slight nod of her head as you say, "Hello Stephanie, I'm very glad to meet you."

"And down at the end of the table we have my good friend John. He's the CEO of one of the world's premier aerospace consulting companies. His specialty is communications and intelligence-gathering satellite systems. John was one of the founders of Universal Aerospacelines. He's on one of our airplanes to somewhere on the planet at least twice a week."

"Next to John, is another good friend of mine—Tyler. Tyler is considered to be a top commercial artist and creative genius. His firm does work for the biggest companies around the globe. He travels on the UA system almost as much as John does, and he's learning to fly at the UA Flight Academy. Oh, did I mention that he also has his own rock band?" Noah asks with a smile. Tyler performs a quick air-guitar rift for you.

"And, of course, on your left is your lovely guide, Toni. You already know that she's a pilot for UA. But what you probably don't know is that she's also my bride," Noah proclaims with an extra-wide grin. "We're not only husband and wife though, we're also business partners and we always fly as a crew. The hard part is deciding who gets to be pilot-in-command," he says with a sly glance in Toni's direction.

When you return your attention to your meal, you notice that your dishes have been cleared away and a lovely apricot sorbet dessert has been placed in front of you. Without any encouragement, you dive into the delight.

As you finish your dessert, Noah offers, "Why don't you sleep on things tonight—I know you must be exhausted by now—so we'll talk again in the morning. I've set you up with a suite over at the Air Travelers' Heaven Resort. It's only a quick hop from here in the AirCenter's helicopter. I know you'll be comfortable there and we can have breakfast around ten. Is that all right with you?"

"Sure," you say, "that'll be great." Noah's words seem to be working on you like a hypnotic spell. Fatigue is washing through your body and you can feel the return of that dream-like feeling.

"Come on," Noah gently commands. "I'll walk you down to the helicopter. It's warming up on the pad right now."

You offer Toni your heartfelt gratitude for her time and attention, and you graciously take your leave of the friendly group of fellow air travelers. You and Noah stroll over to the glass-enclosed elevator shaft, enjoying the view and the room's atmosphere on the way. As you approach the door to the elevator, it automatically opens. You and Noah step inside. The doors close—you are alone with Noah as the elevator begins its decent. The normal feeling of lightened-weight that you experience at the start of a downward elevator run is exaggerated and sustained. You look at Noah with a look of concern.

"Don't let it worry you," Noah says. "The elevator has been programmed to provide the equivalent of one-sixth normal earth gravity for most of the decent. This allows us to feel, albeit for a very short time, what our weight will be on the moon. Everybody loves it!"

You smile back at Noah with a weary, expectant look on your face as the elevator breaks its decent. Noah looks back with that benign look of his and says, "It's been a long day, hasn't it? I think you've done a great job of adjusting to your new circumstances. I know you're going to be at home here in Air Travelers' Heaven. But there is a lot more you must learn about it before we can formally invite you to become a citizen. And we want to learn a lot more about you."

You turn to Noah and say, "I'm still a little confused. It's hard to believe that I'm here. I miss my family and my old world and it's going to take some time to adjust, but I want to be part of this new world and I want to enjoy the benefits of citizenship. You can count on me to give it my best shot to completely understand the vision. I want more than anything else to be aligned with you and all the other Air Travelers' Heaven citizens. I think I can see what you are trying to accomplish and how you are going about it. Please think of me as a person who is thirsting for knowledge and at the same time committed to achieving it."

As the elevator doors glide open, Noah gently places his hand on your shoulder and guides you out of the elevator cab. You can see a helicopter with whirling rotor blades just outside the glass doors leading to the ramp. Before you can open the doors and head out to your waiting ride, Noah stops you. You both turn to face each other, you with a very hopeful look on your face.

Noah says, "I wish you pleasant dreams tonight. Please keep in mind that all the information you are going to need to make a decision to join us is readily available to you. All you have to do is ask. If you need to talk with me tonight, just call the OpsCenter, they'll know how to find me."

You turn towards the glass doors. Noah holds them open. You step through and head for the helicopter. After three paces, you stop and turn back to Noah. The noise from the idling helicopter is deafening. You can smell jet exhaust and feel the beat of the rotor blades in your bones. The rotor disk is stirring up a whirlwind of dust and grass clippings. It is hard for you to see Noah in the still-open doorway, but your eyes meet.

You cup your hands around your mouth and yell, "Don't forget about breakfast tomorrow." Noah once again flashes you his heart-warming smile and shouts back, "I won't. You can count on me."

A sudden feeling of warmth and well-being infuses your soul. You smile back at Noah and turn back to the helicopter. It seems to be straining at the bit, anxious to be airborne once again. You share the feeling.

You step into the well-appointed cabin, and a thought rushes into your consciousness, "I lost my other-world family due to some bad decisions by some good people. But now I have the Air Travelers' Heaven family and I know I'm not going to lose them. Some very good people here are making very-good decisions about air travel. So, I know they'll be as safe as is humanly possible when they fly. I'm confident that I can become a solid citizen of Air Travelers' Heaven. But most importantly, I'm throwing away my false security and drawing some real security in this poker game called 'life'."

The helicopter lifts off the pad and climbs briskly into the night sky. Your spirits are lifted. As you settle into your seat, you think, "I guess I really do belong here in Air Travelers' Heaven."

Chapter 11: "Just The Facts"

"Fearful as reality is, it is less fearful
than evasions of reality."

>Caitlin Thomas
>*"Not Quite Posthumous Letter to My Daughter"*

Christine and I hope that you enjoyed the preceding fictional story. We didn't want to kill off our intrepid air traveler, but we felt that it was the best way for you feel the impact of relying on false security. On the other hand, we brought him/her (can you tell which?) back to life in Air Travelers' Heaven. It seems to be a pretty nice place to live if you travel by air. Our friend was happy—except for the absence of loved ones.

As I pointed out in "Preflight Briefing", the story is based on fact. In this chapter, and throughout the rest of this book, we'll be dealing only with the facts, although I'll also throw in a few opinions related to those facts. As we were reminded in the story, *"false security is just as good as real security, as long as it isn't tested."* We want you to have the facts about your personal safety and security while you are traveling in the U.S. air-transportation system. You can decide for yourself which is the less fearful—false security or real security.

I know that you may be thinking that the story of the "airline trip from hell" endured by our fellow air traveler may be stretching things a little. I haven't been on an airliner for over two years, but I can remember several airline trips out of the thousands that I have taken that, at least in my memory, were worse. I'm certain that many readers will have even more harrowing tales to tell (and we invite you to do just that—see Chapter 13 for details). So, I'd like to ask you, oh gentle reader, to allow me a little literary license if you think I was too hard on our protagonist. Can we not at least agree that the story was a composite of several airline journeys?

You may also think that the airline politics described in the story are more harsh than those found in the real world. Well, my friend, I'm afraid that I have to report to you that the airline politics described in the story really do exist. Some I can attest to as a participant, others I saw first-hand and some I heard or read about. The deregulation of the airline industry in 1979 wrought many changes—most of them, in my opinion, for the worse. The intensity and nature of the relationships between airline managers and pilots took on an entirely new twist with this major shift in the industry.

For example, when I started flying for United Airlines in the pre-deregulation era, a typical airline pilot logged approximately forty hours of flight time during an average month. And he (there were only male airline pilots back then) enjoyed around eighteen days off in every thirty. I believe that if this pre-deregulation schedule were reinstated at the airlines, the safety problems associated with crew fatigue would all but disappear.

Deregulation also brought to the forefront a new breed of manager at U.S. airlines. The airline industry was built by visionary leaders like William A. Patterson at United Air Lines, Juan Trippe at Pan Am, Eddie Rickenbacker at Eastern and C.R. Smith at American. There were still visionary leaders among the top rank of airline management as recently as the early 1980s. One that comes to mind is Percy Wood at United. He provided the exceptional vision that was leading United into the future as the first commercial operator of the Space Shuttle. That is, until the new style of airline manager was able to quash the vision.

These new managers came in with deregulation and they are still here. They focus on making their airline the lowest-cost carrier rather than leading the way into a better future for air travelers. Worrying about the hue of their golden parachutes seems to take up most of their attention. They are anointed as the chosen ones by a board of directors that are similarly distracted, and in many cases a virtual dictatorship is allowed to flourish. A look back at how these new managers have handled the forces unleashed by deregulation, from the perspective of a frequent flyer, reveals a pretty dismal record.

The cramped cabins, the overworked flight- and ground-crews, the virtual gridlock at our busier airports, the overall demoralization of a once-proud workforce, all of these are strong indications that things just aren't working out so well with the type of airline manager we have today. When was the last time that you heard a senior manager at any of the nation's airlines talk about a positive future for you as an air traveler? When was the last time that any of these "leaders" placed an order for an airplane that can fly considerably higher, faster and farther? They're only interested in flying their old airplanes as long as they can, and, when they have to, in buying new airplanes that are cheaper to operate.

On sleepless nights, I can see Juan Trippe turning over in his grave. What must he think of this new breed of airline manager? Would we have ever had the long-range flying boat, the modern jet airliner, the jumbo jet or the supersonic transport if these new managers were in charge of the airline system before 1979? I don't think so.

If the airline industry does not find the courage to place visionary leaders at the top of the major airlines, then I am afraid that the future of airline travel in this country will only continue its long, downhill slide into a mass-transportation system that is doomed to get less efficient and much less enjoyable to use. According to a NASA report, the sad fact is that since deregulation, portal-to-portal travel times in this country have been increasing rather than decreasing. In all of the recorded history of humankind prior to the deregulation of the airline industry, portal-to-portal travel times had been steadily getting shorter.

If we have a dearth of visionary leadership at the airlines, can we not turn to the federal government for the enlightened guidance that will lead us out of this wilderness? I know. I used the terms "government" and "enlightened guidance" in the same sentence. Unfortunately, the arm of the government that is most directly responsible for the mess we are in, the Federal Aviation Administration (FAA), has not been able to provide the direction that we so desperately need.

It is a matter of record that the FAA has *never* completed a major project on-time or on-budget—*never*! We are now faced with the near-meltdown of our air-transportation system. Significant upgrades are urgently needed to solve major problems related to:

air traffic control, airport capacity, safety oversight, airport security and landside facilities. Yet, the FAA drags it bureaucratic feet on making the necessary changes.

As an example of how the FAA responds to a typical safety issue, let's take a look at how they are policing our skies. The FAA has the responsibility for ensuring that pilots, air-traffic controllers, maintenance technicians and all safety-related personnel in the aviation industry are adhering to FAA regulations and safe operating practices.

Before deregulation, a professional in the industry could count on the fact that FAA field personnel were highly qualified, experienced, fair and reasonable people. It was an axiom of the industry that everyone makes mistakes, and that if a mistake is made, it is in everyone's best interest to learn from that mistake rather than merely impose punishment on those unfortunate enough to make one. The goal was always to improve the safety of the system. Of course, if someone was found to be truly negligent in the performance of his/her duties, punitive action was taken. But it was only used for those cases where the FAA believed that remedial action was not justified. In other words, the motto was "cooperate and graduate".

This attitude within the industry worked well for years. I believe that it was a significant contributing factor to the incredible track record of improving safety that the industry chalked up between the late 1920s and the early 1980s. However, this mind-set started to change after deregulation. This transformation was probably due to the increased labor-management tension at the airlines and between FAA management and the air-traffic controllers.

Ronald Reagan busted the controllers union in 1981, Frank Lorenzo busted the Continental pilots' union in 1983, and all the unions at Eastern in 1991. In 1985, Richard Ferris tried, and failed miserably, to bust the pilots' union at United. There were several other significant labor-management disputes during this period and not a few airline failures. Deregulation caused titanic changes in the way the people who manage the airline system in this country and the folks who are on the front lines relate to each other. The change was not for the better.

In my opinion, it was deregulation-caused forces that shifted the FAA's approach to enforcement from one of compassion, leadership and cooperation to one that would be more fitting for the Old West. Around the mid-1980s, aviation professionals (pilots, mechanics, flight attendants and air-traffic controllers) started to take note of the FAA's new attitude. Since that time, the aviation press has been chock full of reports by these very experienced aviation operatives that depict what can only be described as gross injustices committed by the FAA enforcement system.

I can personally attest to the workings of the modern FAA enforcement system. My experience was the result of a flight from Nantucket (KACK) to Newark International Airport (KEWR) that Christine and I flew on July 5, 1999. At that time, we were flying a Cessna Conquest II as a corporate-aircraft crew. Our holiday weekend had been anything but. We had been flying since July 1st and the trip proved to be long, hot and fatiguing.

The two days that we had off while laying over in the hustle and bustle of Hyannis had not fully recharged out batteries by the time we took off for KACK on the morning of July 5th. We had to fly over to KACK from Hyannis early that morning to pick up our two passengers—the aircraft owner's son and daughter-in-law. We were to return to KACK immediately after dropping them off at KEWR to pick up the owner, his wife, his other son and one other passenger. We would then fly back to our home airport with an estimated time of arrival (ETA) of 9 PM.

The passengers were a little late showing up, so we were pressed to make it to KEWR in time for them to make the connection with their airline flight. The flight went relatively smoothly enroute and we were instructed to contact Newark approach control as we approached the New York area. Newark approached acknowledged our sign-on, told us we were in radar contact and told us to expect radar vectors to the final approach course for Runway 22L. I was handling the controls so Christine "rogered" the instructions by repeating them verbatim.

After extensive vectoring, approach control asked us if we had the MD-80 that was turning onto the final approach course for Runway 22L in sight. We told the controller that we did indeed have the MD-80 in sight. He told us to follow it for a visual approach to Runway 22L. Christine acknowledged the fact that we had now been cleared for a visual approach instead of the instrument-landing-system (ILS) approach we had previously been cleared to use.

At the time of the approach, we were in visual meteorological conditions (VMC) with at least three miles of visibility. We were aware, because it was being reported on the KEWR automatic-terminal-information-service (ATIS) frequency, that the active-runway configuration at the airport was set up for landings on Runway 22L and takeoffs on the parallel Runway 22R.

I knew from my many years of flying into KEWR as a United Airlines pilot that this was a common configuration because 22L and 22R were too close together to allow simultaneous parallel approaches to both runways. If aircraft had been making approaches to 22R, KEWR approach would have had to tell us about it when they cleared us for the visual approach to 22L.

As a very experienced pilot, I knew that we had just been led into what could be a very dangerous situation if the proper precautions were not taken. The potential danger was caused by the vortices that are created at the wingtips of all aircraft when they are producing lift—the heavier the airplane, the stronger the vortices. These vortices have been likened to horizontal tornadoes.

The relative weights of the leading and following aircraft also make a big difference in the outcome of a wake-turbulence encounter at low altitude. In this case, the MD-80 weighed well over 100,000 pounds and the Conquest weighed less than 10,000. If we encountered one, or both, of the MD-80's vortices close to the ground, it would probably be impossible to recover before smiting the earth. This would no doubt prove to be fatal to all onboard.

I also knew from my airline-flying days that the pilot of the MD-80 was probably making a steeper-than normal approach on this nice VMC day. This is commonly done to conserve fuel and to reduce noise pollution. However, this technique could easily leave the dreaded vortices laying right on the glidepath to Runway 22L.

I had been well-trained and briefed on wake vortex encounters. They were nothing new. I can remember that when I was teaching my first student pilots how to fly way back in 1965, I was required to brief them on the existence of this particular aeronautical dragon. Over the years since then, I had been deluged with warnings about the phenomenon. My recurrent training at United included briefings on the danger—even a Boeing 737 can get into trouble if it's following a Boeing 747.

As a provider of training to, and an FAA-designated Training Center Evaluator of, corporate pilots, I was required to teach these highly experienced pilots how to recognize and avoid encounters with wake turbulence. I also taught them how to recover from an encounter if one were to take them by surprise. Taken all together, my background, experience and training on the subject of wake-vortex encounters were definitely state-of-the-art.

I applied this knowledge to the situation by planning a flight path that was sure to avoid an encounter with the vortices coming off the MD-80's wingtips. I did this because I am not a test pilot. As far as I know, no one has recovered from a low-altitude encounter with a wingtip vortex in the type aircraft we were flying, and I didn't want to experiment.

Since the wind on the surface was blowing across Runway 22L from right to left, I decided to fly the approach above the glideslope and to the right of the extended Runway 22L centerline. This strategy would keep us above the falling vortices and upwind of the vortex coming off the MD-80's right wingtip (which could drift over the extended centerline with the crosswind from the right).

I also informed Christine that I would touchdown on Runway 22L beyond the point where the MD-80 landed. This would keep us above its vortices when we got close to the ground. Once the MD-80 had landed and its wings were no longer producing lift, the vortices would disappear.

I briefed Christine on this decision and she concurred. We were both very clear that we were making a visual approach to Runway 22L and that our strategy would allow us to avoid the MD-80's wingtip vortices.

I flew the final approach to 22L as briefed, flying an offset final approach course to the west of the extended 22L centerline. I was not concerned about being close to the 22R final approach course because I knew there was no traffic on approach to that runway and that the runway center lines were only about one-thousand feet apart.

I knew of no regulation that prohibited me from flying to the right of the 22L centerline on a visual approach, and I knew that I was not interfering with other traffic. Therefore, I did not see a need to ask for an amended clearance from approach control or the tower. What I was doing was really common practice in a situation like this. I did not think we were doing anything out of the ordinary.

My plan was to stay to the right of 22L until we were one-to-two miles from the threshold, and then to align the airplane with 22L and land about two-thousand feet down the 9,980-foot-long runway. There would still be plenty of room to land since the Conquest needed less than two-thousand feet for its ground roll.

As we approached the airport, we saw an aircraft depart 22R and a Boeing 737 pull into position on that runway. I was obviously not going to land on top of, or fly over at very-low altitude, the airliner on 22R. I was clearly going to land on 22L.

Christine and I did not know it at the time, but the tower controller who had issued us a landing clearance on 22L was watching us as we stayed to the right of the extended 22L centerline. At no time did he, as would be common practice, ask us if we really knew which runway we were going to land on. As it turned out, he was confused, but we weren't.

Approximately two miles from the approach end of 22L, just as I was making a left bank to align us with its centerline, the tower controller ordered us to go around. We immediately complied with his instructions to pull up, make a right-hand traffic pattern and then land on 22R. This was accomplished without further incident.

As we were taxing in, I mentioned to Christine that we had probably been sent around because it is all too typical at large airports for tower controllers to assume that private airplanes are piloted by idiots. I commented that the controller probably had a mistaken belief that we were going to land on 22R when we had been cleared to land on 22L. My suspicions were confirmed a few seconds later when the ground controller told us to call the tower supervisor after we parked the airplane.

We sent our passengers scurrying for their airline flight and I went into the fixed-base operator (FBO) to call the tower. When the tower chief came on the line, I could tell that he had an "attitude". However, he was forthcoming in telling me that at no time had minimum traffic-separation standards been violated during our approach, go around and subsequent landing. In other words, there was no problem. Now, we pilots have a belief that if you hear the words "Hi, I'm from the FAA and I'm here to help you", one should take immediate evasive action. So, I tried to establish some rapport with the FAA supervisor in an attempt to forestall any divergent views of the situation.

I told him that although I was flying a small, twin-engine turboprop on this particular day, I had flown into KEWR many times as a pilot for United. This, I hoped, would let him know that he was not dealing with a private pilot who was in way over his head in flying into one of the nation's busiest airports. I also briefed him on my strategy to avoid the MD-80's wake vortices since I was by now suspecting that he was going to accuse me of trying to land on the wrong runway.

By the end of conversation, I felt that the tower chief and I had reached the mutual conclusion that the tower controller had misread my intentions. We also seemed to be in agreement that I knew what I was doing and that the incident was nothing to get excited about. No harm was done and no one was even inconvenienced, except us.

Prior to this event, the last time that I had a conversation of a similar vein with a tower chief was probably thirty-plus years beforehand. That situation had resolved itself with no further communication from the FAA. The tone of my conversation with the KEWR tower chief led me to believe that things would be resolved in the same manner this time. As I walked away from the phone, I recalled the articles I had been reading about an FAA enforcement system that had run amuck, and I thought that the writers must have been exaggerating. It looked to me like the system was working like it always had—with goodwill and common sense.

A couple of days later, I got a call from an FAA inspector assigned to the Teterboro, New Jersey Flight Standards District Office (FSDO). He told me that he was investigating a Preliminary Pilot Deviation Report that had been filed with his office by the KEWR tower. Of course, I knew immediately what the call was about. After getting over my initial disappointment that the tower chief had misled me, I told the inspector that I would fully cooperate with him in his investigation.

After I explained the situation to him, he indicated that he could see that I knew what I was doing and that I had followed the prudent course of action by avoiding the MD-80's wake vortices. He asked me to put the explanation in writing and forward it to him. Once again, I came away from the conversation with the opinion that we were all just going through the normal bureaucratic steps that were required to clear up the paperwork.

On August 6, 1999, I sent my letter to the FAA inspector and fully expected that I wouldn't hear any more about the incident. A few days later, I received a letter from the inspector that was dated before my letter to him. It officially informed me that I was being investigated for a possible violation of the Federal Aviation Regulations (FARs). Needless to say, I was shocked. In my thirty-four years (at that time) of professional flying, I had never even been under suspicion of violating the FARs. And I certainly had not had any kind of certificate action taken against me. It would be an understatement to say that at this point I was very frustrated. It appeared that the bureaucrats were going to press the issue despite what I thought was a very reasonable explanation of the incident.

Christine and I are both members of the Aircraft Owners and Pilots Association (AOPA). I have been a member on-and-off for many years. Christine is a 12-year member. AOPA's membership numbers in the six figures. It represents the interests of private-aircraft owners and pilots, and it does a great job of keeping its members informed about what's happening in the aviation world. It also offers a legal-defense service that Christine and I had subscribed to just before this incident. When we signed up, we didn't really think we were going to need it, but now the AOPA attorney was the next person on my call list.

When I talked with the AOPA attorney about the problem, he asked me who the FAA inspector was. When I told him, his response was "Oh, oh. You're in trouble. He's a 'badge and gun' type of guy." I then asked the attorney what he meant. He told me that the FAA had been hiring many new inspectors in the prior few years, and that this person had been one of them. He said that this particular inspector was notorious for his lack of reasonableness and his desire to "violate" any pilot who came to his attention through the FAA enforcement process. I knew then that it was highly likely that my pilot certificate would be suspended.

Things were quiet until early October, but then I received a Notice Of Proposed Certificate Action from an FAA attorney. It informed me that unless I availed myself of the FAA appeals process, my pilot certificate would be suspended within fifteen days. The proposed suspension was for thirty days. It was time to call in the attorneys.

The chief AOPA attorney referred me to an AOPA-affiliated New Jersey attorney to handle my case. As it turned out, the attorney was an old professional acquaintance of mine, Eddie Hadden. Eddie had been a pilot for Eastern airlines until Frank Lorenzo killed the company.

I had met Eddie in 1986 when I was among a contingent of Air Line Pilots Association (ALPA) volunteers who went to Atlanta to help the Eastern pilots get ready for an anticipated strike against their airline. I have always had a very high level of respect for the pilots of Eastern Airlines. They reciprocated this feeling in 1986 when they officially made me an honorary Eastern pilot.

I was very relieved to know that Eddie would be helping me out. Unfortunately, Eddie had the same reaction as the AOPA attorney. He also believed that the FAA inspector who was investigating the incident was prone to charge pilots with a violation at the drop of a hat.

Eddie did a great job of representing me with the FAA. He ably pleaded my case and used his professional pilot background to corroborate the strategy I had used to avoid the MD-80's wingtip vortices. Alas, it was to no avail. As it turns out, the FAA's internal appeals process is really just eyewash. The poor pilot who has found himself unjustly ensnared in the FAA enforcement process has only an FAA attorney assigned to the investigating inspector's office to appeal to. If that appeal is unsuccessful, the pilots only other option is an appeal to the National Transportation Safety Board (NTSB).

Now I don't know if this seems unfair to you, but to me the FAA's internal-appeals process is just a typical example of a "bureaucratic shuffle". To my mind, it is highly unlikely that one bureaucrat will overturn the decision of another public servant if there is no compelling reason to do so. In fact, the motivation of both the inspector and the reviewing attorney are to make the charge stick so that their records look better.

We held the appeal meeting via conference call, so I never got a chance to look either the FAA attorney or the inspector in the eye. Eddie and I argued my case, but the FAA folks weren't even listening. Finally, in frustration I asked the inspector about his aviation background because both Eddie and I felt that my decision to take wake-vortex-avoidance precautions was really a judgment call. I wanted to know what kind of expertise he had that gave him the confidence to decide that my decision was worthy of a certificate suspension. The FAA inspector was very vague about his aviation background, but it became clear that he was primarily a light-airplane pilot with limited experience.

This confirmed my suspicions and shocked me at the same time. One would think that a light-airplane pilot would be especially sensitive to the need to avoid wake turbulence. It was also clear to Eddie and me that someone with his obviously limited background should not put his judgment before that of someone with the world's best pilot training and over three-decades of flying behind him. Alas, Eddie's eloquent arguments and my request that the FAA attorney provide a little reasonable thinking fell on deaf ears.

It was very obvious that the case turned on a judgment call, and that the FAA was going to go with their judgment. In the "good old days", this would never have happened. Even if a FAA inspector disagreed with a pilot's decision, due weight would be given to the pilot's intentions and the fact that no one was put in danger and no traffic-separation standards had been violated. Back when the FAA was populated by reasonable airmen, the most that would have happened would have been the imposition of a requirement for some remedial training. I am convinced that had the incident happened before the FAA's shift from common sense to senseless enforcement, the whole problem would have ended with my conversation with the tower chief.

An interesting factor that came out in the discovery phase of the appeal process was the revelation that the KEWR tower controller who had sent us around that day was in fact a trainee. This cleared up the question of why the tower controller had not simply asked us what our intentions were when he became nervous about our ground track. This would normally be the first thing an experienced controller would do.

We found another pertinent fact on an FAA document called a "Personnel Statement" that had been submitted by one of the other controllers on duty in the KEWR tower at the time of the incident. She simply confirmed the fact that the local controller had issued a go-around order to us and then she clearly stated that "I reserve the right to change this statement as more information becomes available". This indicates to me that possibly this controller did not believe that the filing of a pilot deviation report was proper. Maybe she was a pilot. Before PATCO was busted, most air-traffic controllers were pilots. This is not the case today.

On April 5, 2000, the FAA made their final decision on the case. An FAA attorney issued an Order of Suspension. My certificate was suspended for thirty days. I decided not to appeal the case to the NTSB because Eddie advised me that the board usually sided with the FAA, and because the process would be very costly and time-consuming.

I hated to make that decision. I did not like the fact that my unsullied flying record would be marred by this patently unfair suspension, but the bottom line was that dropping the matter at that point was the pragmatic thing to do. Part of me wants to go back and change that decision, but it would have undoubtedly been just an exercise in frustration.

This may sound to you like just another case of "pilot whining". You do know the difference between a jet airliner and a jet-airliner pilot, don't you? When the jet airliner reaches the gate and its engines are shutdown, it stops whining. The pilot doesn't. This is an old airline joke. However, I believe the implications of this story are far-reaching.

First of all, any air-traffic controller can file a pilot-deviation report on any pilot, but no pilot can file a "controller-deviation report" (one doesn't exist) on an air-traffic controller. If a pilot thinks that a controller should be investigated for a deviation from safe operating practices, his/her only option is to send a letter to the controller's supervisor. I'm sure you share my opinion of where that letter is going to end up. Yet, a pilot-deviation report can have a major adverse effect on the pilot's career. This kind of unfairness only exacerbates the growing tensions between pilots and air-traffic controllers at a time when the stresses on the system desperately mandate that they work together to ensure a safe flight.

Also, it is pretty obvious to me that the KEWR tower chief was covering his own tail by filing the pilot-deviation report. The trainee-controller had made a mistake by not asking us about our intentions before he issued the go-around order (in my opinion). It is common knowledge that air-traffic-control specialists, and their supervisors, are under tremendous pressure to "push tin" (Have you seen the movie *"Pushing Tin"*? You should. In my opinion it accurately portrays the life of an air-traffic controller).

Sending an aircraft around is not conducive to the expeditious movement of airplanes on-and-off an airport. It is my suspicion that the tower chief was going to have to explain to his supervisor why we had been issued the go-around order. My experience leads me to believe that any good bureaucrat will first try to lay blame off on someone else before he/she takes it upon his/her own shoulders.

I don't know about you, but I'm not looking to the government for the leadership we need. The actions of this huge bureaucracy over the past two decades have left most of the professionals in the aviation industry frustrated and despondent. I do not believe that any meaningful leadership will be forthcoming from the FAA.

I'd like to touch on another fact-based element of the story about Air Travelers' Heaven—pilot pushing. As I'm sure you will recall, our copilot's father had a medical problem that was causing him to frequently put himself on his airline's pilot sick list; and that the airline was pressuring him to fly despite the condition. Pilot pushing has been a causal factor in several airline accidents and incidents—it is a very dangerous practice.

Airline managers are motivated to push pilots beyond reasonable personal limits for many reasons. The obvious ones are greed and a need to control others. A less-subtle motivation can be found in that old human demon—envy. Many, if not all, airline managers think of pilots as "labor". Many of these managers are also quite jealous of the compensation and time off these "laborers" enjoy. In most cases, even relatively junior pilots are paid more than mid-level managers.

Therefore, the managers have a tendency to take a hard line when it comes to pilots who use their sick-leave option "too often". Most airline managers will tell you that "too often" is more than two times per year. Obviously, a pilot with a chronic medical problem will probably need to use sick leave more often than that. If a manager pressures a pilot to fly while he/she is debilitated by an impairing condition, then that manager is engaging in pilot pushing.

Unfortunately, in the airline industry, pilot pushing is real. It has been going on since the dawn of the airlines. The bad news is that it is contrary to good operating practices because it is also very dangerous. In Chapter 12, we'll take a close look at what other pilots are saying about this problem. But first, I would like to share a personal story with you. I think my story will convince you that pilot pushing is a real problem, and not just a fictional device that I used to make our copilot's story more interesting.

The personal story of pilot pushing that I am going to tell you is only one of many that I could acquaint you with. I have been on the receiving end of pilot pushing many times, and I have heard other stories from the hundreds of pilots that I've flown with. My story of pilot pushing is much like the one I created for our copilot's father, only it's real. It began not long after deregulation took effect.

The story begins with a medical problem that appeared shortly after I was promoted to first officer. The symptom was an intense, piercing pain in my right inner ear. When the condition was flaring up, it felt like someone was slowly twisting an ice pick into my eardrum. The pain was so distracting that I couldn't properly fulfill my flying duties.

The condition only appeared in the latter days of the long trips I was flying for United. Once it started, it would normally persist if I continued with the trip. However, after a couple of days off, it would disappear. When I went back to flying, I would suffer a reoccurrence of the symptom.

After a few of these cycles, I started putting myself on sick leave whenever the pain got too bad. I felt that I was obligated to do this not only out of concern for my passengers' safety, but also because the FAA says that I have to.

Federal Aviation Regulations (FARs), Part 61.53 states that a pilot must ground himself if he *"Knows or has reason to know of any medical condition that would make the person unable to meet the requirements for the medical certificate necessary for the pilot operation..."* This regulation, like most other FARs, is open to interpretation.

To my knowledge, most pilots interpret this FAR to mean that they must ground themselves if they have a medical condition that would disqualify them for a medical certificate if, at the time they're applying for the certificate, they are experiencing the condition. I believed that if I told an FAA Aviation Medical Examiner that I had debilitating pain in my inner ear, he would not give me a medical certificate until the condition cleared up. Therefore, I felt obligated under this FAR to ground myself whenever I was scheduled to fly and the condition was flaring up.

Pilots are also legally required to operate under the tenets laid out in the Aeronautical Information Manual which is published by the FAA. Chapter 8, "Medical Facts For Pilots", Section 1, "Fitness For Flight", paragraphs 8-1-1, b, 1 and 2 state:

"Even a minor illness suffered in day-to-day living can seriously degrade performance of many piloting tasks vital to safe flight. Illness can produce fever and distracting symptoms that can impair judgment, memory, alertness, and the ability to make calculations. Although symptoms from an illness may be under adequate control with a medication, the medication itself may decrease pilot performance."

"The safest rule is not to fly while suffering from any illness. If this rule is considered too stringent for a particular illness, the pilot should contact an Aviation Medical Examiner for advice."

The United Airlines Flight Operations Manual also mandated that a pilot not fly if he or she was not fit for duty. It was very clear to me that I was obligated under the FARs, company policy and common sense to ground myself when this intense pain was debilitating me.

United's policy at the time was to call a pilot in for a little talk with his/her flight manager whenever sick-leave usage passed a certain point. When I was called into his office to explain why I had been on the sick list so often, I dutifully reported the nature of my problem to my supervisor. He told me to report to the company doctor to have the problem checked out.

The company doctor told me that he didn't know what the problem was and that I should "quit malingering and go back to work." I did as I was ordered. The next time I had the problem, I reported to the doctor and asked him to put me on the sick list. He refused. We went around this bush several times before he finally sent me to a specialist.

My first visit to the specialist revealed that the mysterious medical condition that the company doctor could not diagnose was actually a common problem. It is referred to as a TMJ problem. It is caused when there is a dysfunction of the temporomandibular joint—the joint connecting the lower jaw bone to the skull.

The specialist told me that many people have pain and/or dysfunction in and around the jaw joint at some point during their lives. Symptoms can affect the jaw and jaw joint as well as muscles in the face, shoulder and neck. He told me that a TMJ problem could easily manifest itself as an intense pain in the inner ear.

He also told me that the most common cause of the symptoms is muscle tension which often occurs in response to stress. Stress-related habits include clenching or grinding one's teeth. This bad habit can tire the jaw muscles and lead to a cycle of spasm, tissue damage, pain, muscle tenderness and more spasm. Approximately 12% of TMJ sufferers develop chronic symptoms. Any chronic pain, or difficulty moving the jaw, may affect talking, eating and swallowing, thus affecting a person's overall sense of well-being. And chronic pain can lead to depression, anxiety, a sense of helplessness and biochemical changes in the body that perpetuate pain. Therefore, it is important to have long-lasting pain evaluated and treated.

When the specialist explained all this to me, a light bulb came on in my mind. Of course, flying a jet airliner is a very stressful situation. I had a propensity to clench my jaw whenever I was stressed. I unknowingly clenched my jaw while I was flying the jet and that triggered the pain. It all fit. I was relieved to finally know that the pain was not being caused by a mysterious brain tumor. The next thing I wanted to know was how to fix the problem.

The specialist informed me that treatment of TMJ disorder symptoms may include resting the jaw joint, short-term use of anti-inflammatory medications or muscle relaxants, physical therapy and stress-reduction-skills training. Of course, the medications were out of the question. I couldn't use them while flying. I was left with resting the jaw joint, physical therapy and stress-reduction-skills training.

The doctor told me that he didn't think physical therapy would be effective in my case, so I was down to two possible solutions. The first, resting the jaw joint, would require me to continue to use sick leave whenever the pain reared its ugly head. The second, stress-reduction techniques, I could learn over time.

The specialist reported his findings to the company doctor. The company doctor told me to learn how to relax and to get back to work. I worked on my stress-reduction skills. I eventually found meditation to be very helpful, but it took me several years to learn how to apply it in real-time to stop the pain. Meanwhile, I continued to put myself on the sick list whenever I felt that it was necessary. Not much was said about my use of sick leave for a couple of years, but then things changed considerably.

In late 1984 and early 1985, I was helping the United pilots prepare for a possible strike. Based upon some very good intelligence, we believed that we were being forced into a strike by Richard Ferris. He was, at the time, United's CEO. It was reported to us that Ferris was doing this in an effort to prove that he was as tough as Frank Lorenzo, CEO of Continental Airlines. Ferris, we were told, wanted to break the pilot's union at United just as Lorenzo had at Continental.

I was a highly visible member of the strike-preparation committee. In the years prior to this time, I had become rather well-known at the airline through various things that I had done for the pilots and for the company. I had been Chairman of the UAL-ALPA Professional Outlook Committee, a special assistant to the president of United (for Space Shuttle acquisition), the National Chairman of the American Society of Aerospace Pilots and I had played many other roles. This high visibility made me one of the opinion makers in the pilot group.

As preparations for a strike were intensifying in both camps in early 1985, I received a letter from United Airlines informing me that I had been fired for misuse of sick leave. No preliminary charges. No hearings. No progressive discipline as is called for under the pilot contract. No recognition of the TMJ diagnosis and the company doctor's involvement in it. No acknowledgement of the fact that I was on the sick list—placed there by the company doctor—at the time of my termination. Nothing—just a short letter telling me that I was no longer welcome at United Airlines. Only one other United pilot, who was also a highly visible strike-preparation-committee member, received a termination letter at that time.

Fortunately for me, the United pilots were truly that—united—in their cause. As the history books describe the strike, the pilots won hands down. The back-to-work agreement that was negotiated to end the strike included amnesty for me and the other pilot.

After the strike, I went back to work. A short time later, my TMJ problem came back and I started to put myself on the sick list again while I sought a solution to the problem. This time, however, whenever I went on sick leave a specified number of times (I think it was five), the company sent me a letter informing me that I was being processed through a progressive-discipline protocol that would ultimately lead to my termination as a United pilot if I continued to use sick leave.

It was clear to me and my contemporaries that United management was out to get rid of me because of my union activities during the strike. It didn't seem to matter to them that they were trying to force me to violate the FARs and company policy—although I pointed this out to them at every opportunity. The cycle of sick leave use, reprimand letters, hearings and threats continued for almost five years.

The company had me in a tight spot. If I continued to ground myself for the TMJ condition they would fire me. If I flew with the condition, the FAA could pull my medical certificate and charge me with violating the FARs.

United's managers also had put themselves in a corner. If they didn't fire me at the end of the progressive-discipline process, a precedent would be set for the use of sick leave by the pilots. This new precedent would undoubtedly cost the company many millions of dollars. This would not look good on their resumes. On the other hand, they knew that their charges against me were bogus and not really defensible. I had made it clear to them that I would appeal a termination decision to the National Labor Relations Board. In all likelihood, my appeal would result in my reinstatement with back pay (after an estimated three years). This also would not look good to their bosses.

Needless to say, by the time things were coming to a head in late 1989, emotions were running high on both sides of the issue. Certain events that may, or may not, have been similar to those our copilot's father experienced, transpired and I made the decision to resign from United Airlines in January of 1990 at the age of forty-two.

It was the hardest decision I've ever made. United had first told me that they were going to hire me when I was nineteen years old. When I turned twenty-one, they did (21 is the minimum age for a pilot at a major airline) and I considered it my home. My mother worked for United as did one of my brothers, his wife and several hundred of my friends. I never applied to another airline. I poured a tremendous part of my heart and soul into United Airlines—on many fronts. I had planned on flying for Untied until I was sixty, then enjoying a wonderful retirement. It was definitely hard to leave, but it was the best decision to make under the circumstances.

To my mind, this is a clear case of pilot pushing. In this instance, it was for political reasons. If I had allowed the United managers to intimidate me, I would have flown hundreds of trips carrying thousands of passengers while I was not fit to fly. I am convinced that pilot pushing is endemic in the airline industry. In the next chapter, you'll see reports from many other pilots about this little-talked-about threat to your safety.

So far in this chapter, we've looked closely at some of the more-interesting facts upon which our story is based. I hope that you are convinced that these are real problems that affect your personal safety and the enjoyment of your flying experiences. There are many additional safety- and convenience-related issues that are raised in the story. They too are real problems. We have compiled the following list of these issues. We invite you to visit our Web site *(www.aerospacetrust.com)* to explore them in detail.

1. the hub-and-spoke system's effect on portal-to-portal travel times
2. enhanced-vision systems (EVS)
3. alcohol consumed aboard aircraft
4. current security as it affects portal-to-portal travel times
5. the real effectiveness of current security
6. landside infrastructure crowding now and in the future
7. airline on-time performance
8. lack of service on airlines
9. theft in terminals
10. bag screening
11. lack of responsiveness of airline reservations centers
12. lack of direct flights
13. air quality in airliners
14. flight overbooking
15. effect of pilot experience on safety
16. effect of crew-pairing on safety
17. management pilots flying the line
18. effects of pilot-management relationships on safety
19. effects of pilot types on safety
20. effects of copilot assertiveness on safety
21. effects of turbulence close to the ground
22. effects of obstructions on and around airports
23. black-hole approaches
24. non-precision approaches
25. hydroplaning
26. effects of ground-spoiler non-deployment
27. effects of reverse thrust in strong cross winds on slippery runways
28. rules on fuel requirements

29.   pilot decision making
30.   cockpit confusion
31.   lack of up-to-date safety technology in airliners
32.   missed approaches
33.   challenge-response checklists
34.   negative panic
35.   effects of decreased seat pitch on safety
36.   g-force effects in a crash
37.   factors effecting emergency egress from an airliner cabin
38.   lack of impairment testing

I can assure you that each of these issues has a significant affect on your safety and comfort when you are using the airline system. If just a few of the safety-related issues are encountered in combination on a single flight, disaster could be the result. You owe it to yourself and your loved ones to be fully informed about these threats to your well-being. Your real security depends upon it.

There are some other issues that are raised in the story that I'd also like to briefly discuss. Again, you can visit our Web site at *www.aerospacetrust.com* for more information on these topics.

1.   The aerospaceplane: It would be feasible right now if the necessary propulsion technology were in hand. Many people believe that this technology is already flying in a military version of the vehicle. If so, we need to demilitarize it. If not, we need to drive the development of this technology only a little to achieve single-stage-to-orbit capability.

2.   Traveling to-and-from the moon in a safe, reliable and affordable manner: The aerospaceplane is the

cornerstone of such a system. The other elements are well within the capabilities of our current technology.

3. Settling the moon: Once again, the aerospaceplane is critical to accomplishing this feet. Otherwise, I know of no other technological barriers to doing it right now.

4. Water on the moon: It's there. NASA confirmed in 1998 that there are vast amounts of water-ice in craters near the moon's two poles.

5. Koch Crater: It's there too. It's located at 42.8° South Latitude/150.1° East Longitude. It is 75 kilometers in diameter.

6. Captain Toni Pilot: I used to serve in the National Guard with a TWA pilot who's real name was Jerry Pilot (are you still out there Jerry?).

7. Hippies in Denver in 1978: I swear that I saw some.

8. The marketing guru mentioned in Chapter 10 is also a real person. His name is Steve Caler and he's the CEO of Caler&Company, a marketing and design firm based in Akron, Ohio. Steve and his team are providing the design and marketing expertise for AvWorld which you will read about in Chapter 13.

In the next chapter, we're going to turn to other pilots, aviation professionals and other experts for their input on the reality of many of these issues. We sincerely want you to be as safe as possible when you are voyaging in the medium we love—the sky. In the next chapter you will discover that we are not alone.

Chapter 12: "Flying Blind"

*"He knew that we gave constant lip service to the dictates of safety
and howled like Christians condemned to the arena if any compromise
were made of it. He knew we were seekers after ease, suspicious, egotistic,
and stubborn to a fault. He also knew that none of us would have continued
our careers unless we had always been, and still were,
helpless before this opportunity to take a chance."*

> *Ernest K. Gann*
> *about professional pilots in*
> *"Fate Is The Hunter"*

Pilots are risk takers. There is no doubt about that. Every time we fly, we take our fate, and those of our passengers, into our own hands. One of my instructors in Army-helicopter-pilot training always reminded me of a truism whenever I got a little over confident with my new-found rotary-wing skills. The maxim was that every time the human body gets more than ten-feet off the ground, or moves over the ground at more than ten miles-per-hour, it is subject to severe damage up to and including death. We pilots know that if we are going to take risks, we have to manage them properly, for the outcome of a poor decision can ruin our whole day.

Modern aviation is a marvel. The Wright Brothers invented a practical way for us to fly only one-hundred years ago. Since that time, flight has progressed from an almost-certain death activity to an incredibly safe mass-transportation system. The vehicles we fly in are extremely reliable. The high-tech systems that support our flights of fancy are unbelievably dependable, given their complexity. Christine and I believe that the performance of the humans who run our air-transportation system is the last air-safety frontier to be conquered.

Most aviation-safety experts will tell you that seventy-to-eighty percent of all air crashes are caused by human error. Clearly, we must do everything we can to reduce the number of accidents that are a result, at least in part, of an avoidable mistake.

Technological advances will help, but those that do will mainly be involved with the human-machine interface and communications. The real advances that will reduce the accident rate will be aimed at adjusting the system to better fit the limitations of its operators. Some of these adjustments will involve turning the clock back to a saner time, as is the case with crew rest and duty times. Others will require a new look at how the airlines are managing their human resources.

This chapter is going to focus primarily on pilot impairment. If you are an impaired pilot, as you will see, you may be classified as "blind drunk" even though you have not taken even a sip of alcohol for several years. Many aviation experts believe that if the problem of pilot impairment is properly addressed and good solutions are put into place, the aviation accident rate will be reduced dramatically.

To back up this statement, and to get other perspectives on these important air-safety issues, we're going to call upon our fellow aviation professionals to help us out. Up to this point, you have been reading about the issues through our personal filters. We think you should see what others are saying about a few of the more-worrisome problems.

Most of what follows comes from pilots and/or the professionals who have reason to study various aspects of pilot personality and mental performance. We have a very high level of confidence that the reports by these pilots are open, honest and clear. How can we be so certain? It is because the code of ethics followed by all pilots mandates the use of these principles when interacting with other aviation professionals.

This policy is taught, both formally and informally, to all aspiring pilots. If a pilot is anything less than open, honest and clear, the other aviation professionals with whom he/she interacts, will ostracize him/her. And our accepted standard operating practices are designed to foster these principles at all times, even when executing a checklist.

So, if you can agree with us that these reports are reliable, let's turn to them for more enlightenment. We're going to take a detailed look at pilot impairment in this chapter. Now, if you're like most people, when you hear the words "pilot impairment", you think of pilots who are found to have been drinking when they shouldn't be.

However, you know from our fictional story that there are many other causes of impairment. Alcohol abuse is probably the least of our worries in terms of the number of times pilots fly while impaired by alcohol versus the almost ubiquitous instances of pilots flying while under the impairing effects of fatigue, stress and personal problems.

Pilot Suicide

I'm sure you recall this quote from Chapter 3: *"You also didn't know that this particular captain had a secret even his copilot didn't know about. Three years ago, he had tried to kill himself." "He entered the airline's employee assistance program and, two years later, he was back flying for the airline again."*

Did you think that pilots don't commit suicide? Guess again! Why should they be less susceptible than anyone else? Pilots may be highly intelligent and well-trained professionals, but they are just human beings after all.

Commercial pilots are faced with many problems that are not found in most professions. Pilots often have long (12-16 hour) stress-filled duty days, many nights away from home on layovers, and schedules that do not promote quality time at home with one's spouse and children.

These things often contribute to domestic discord and divorce. Hence, the all too familiar line among commercial pilots that states, "I suffer from AIDS—Aviation Induced Divorce Syndrome." Not surprisingly, divorce is a major risk factor associated with suicide. I cannot bring to mind many airline pilots that I personally know who have not gone through at least one divorce while actively serving as a commercial pilot. Before we hear from others on this issue, I'd like to share three accounts of pilot suicide that I personally know about.

For many years, Christine and I had a friendship with a duo who were one of those much-envied "never divorced couples"—that is, until about three years ago. Both of them are pilots. The husband is a captain for a major U.S. airline. After at least two decades of marriage, they decided to untie the knot.

During the two-plus years of an ugly divorce battle, the wife regularly placed concerned calls to mutual friends and the family of her estranged husband. Why? Because the good captain was severely depressed and constantly calling to tell her that life wasn't worth living anymore, and that he was going to kill himself.

She was truly terrified that he would commit suicide via airplane and take a lot of innocent people along with him. Did he? Not as of the publication of this book. However, to my knowledge, he never took himself off of the flying schedule when he was having a severe episode of depression either. I don't know that he ever sought professional help or availed himself of the services of his company's Employee Assistance Program (EAP).

This is an airline accident looking for a place to happen. Luckily it hasn't yet. Will he be one of the fifty-percent of those depressed individuals who become dejected more than once? Could he be one of the ten-percent that experience manic phases in addition to the depressive ones?

We do know that many suicide attempts are carried out impulsively. An April 8, 2002 report in *Reuters Health* points out, *"Almost one in four Americans who survive a nearly lethal suicide attempt spent fewer than 5 minutes between making the decision to attempt suicide and carrying out the act, according to researchers."* And that *"The researchers further observed that while alcohol use, race, education and marital status played no special role in the likelihood of impulsive suicides, male patients were almost twice as likely as female patients to make an impulsive suicide attempt— 31% versus 16%. Impulsive attempts, they noted, were more likely to occur at night and to involve more violent means, such as guns, hanging, cutting and jumping."* (airplane crashes?)

The article also noted that *"Those who tended to be depressed or felt hopeless, however, appeared to be less likely to make an impulsive attempt—leaving the researchers to suggest that current risk-screening for suicide may be too narrowly focused on signs of long-running depression rather than shorter-term emotional problems".* I don't know which is scarier, thinking that a pilot might impulsively carry out a suicide attempt while I'm riding in the back as a passenger, or wondering if he/she has been plotting his/her demise via airplane for some time.

The other two accounts that I'd like to share with you go back to 1990. Just before I resigned from United Airlines, two fellow United pilots made their individual confessions to me that they had tried to commit suicide at a time when they were regularly flying for United. The good news is that the attempts were not made while they were on the job. The circumstance surrounding these confessions was emotionally charged. I have no doubt that they were telling me the truth. I had known these gentlemen both professionally and socially for years. Their revelations were a shock to me.

I don't think either knew that the other one had told me about his suicide attempt, but their stories were eerily similar. At the time they made the attempt on their own lives, they were both going through some very difficult personal and family problems. Both of them had obviously been unsuccessful in their attempts. And both of them, subsequent to the attempts, had gone through a United Airlines-sponsored, FAA-approved (I assume) rehabilitation program and then returned to line flying. As far as you or I know, one of these gentlemen could be the captain of your next flight.

We don't know how many airline pilots flying today have attempted to commit suicide. I know of the two that were personally reported to me, and the one former friend who was surely a likely candidate. Christine spent many hours scouring available airline and FAA records for documented cases of pilot suicides. The instances reported below are all that she could find. There are no direct mentions of any FAA-approved programs that these pilots are put through before they are returned to flying. If you are a conspiracy-theory aficionado, you may interpret this lack of openness as a cover up.

The airlines have no way of knowing about a pilot's emotional state unless co-workers are willing to "tattle", or the pilot turns himself in. The airlines usually don't check their pilots for mental impairment. The closest they come is in the form of an FAA flight physical which is administered, at best, twice a year. The examinations are performed by an FAA-certified Aviation Medical Examiner (AME). These physical exams do not typically include an in-depth psychological evaluation.

To find out what the FAA does have to say on the subject, let's turn once again to the Aeronautical Information Manual (AIM). In the chapter "Medical Facts for Pilots", there is a paragraph on emotion that states:

> *"Certain emotionally upsetting events, including a serious argument, death of a family member, separation or divorce, loss of a job, and financial catastrophe, can render a pilot unable to fly an aircraft*

safely. The emotions of anger, depression, and anxiety from such events not only decrease alertness but also may lead to taking risks that border on self-destruction. Any pilot who experiences an emotionally upsetting event should not fly until satisfactorily recovered from it."

Another arm of the federal government, the National Transportation Safety Board (NTSB), has listed pilot suicide as a causal, or possibly causal, factor in its reports on several accidents. The most recent accident that was attributed to pilot suicide was Egypt Air Flight 990 that occurred in 1999. The death toll in that headlong crash into the ocean was 217 souls.

There are many other accidents that could be interpreted as being caused by pilot suicide. Some accidents that had mysterious antecedents could also be attributed to this cause. Let's turn now to some reports by other pilots.

Kenneth A. Cubbin is a flight engineer for Qantas. He began his career with this major international airline more than 25 years ago. The following excerpts are from his article *"To Die For"* that appeared on a popular aviation Web site called AvWeb (*www.avweb.com*) in 2002.

✓From an article titled *"The Neurobiology of Depression" published in the June 1998 issue of "Scientific American." At the time the article was published, its author, Charles B. Nemeroff, was professor and chairman of the Department of Psychiatry and Behavioral Sciences at the Emory University School of Medicine.*

Professor Nemeroff suggests: "5 to 12 percent of men and 10 to 20 percent of women in the U.S. will suffer from a major depressive episode at some time in their life. Roughly half of these individuals will become depressed more than once, and up to 10 percent (about 1.0 to 1.5 percent of Americans) will experience manic phases in addition to depressive ones...As many as 15 percent of those who suffer from depression or bipolar disorder commit suicide each year."

✓ *In what may be a very disturbing statistic in relation to pilot suicide, Professor Nemeroff contends that "many people who kill themselves do so in a way that allows another diagnosis to be listed on the death certificate, so that families can receive insurance benefits or avoid embarrassment."*

✓ *In my airline career, I have known of only two crewmembers who ultimately lost their job....Both of these pilots were commonly known to have severe drinking problems, but none of their peers complained to management nor refused to fly with them.*

✓ *However, since the FAA will not allow a pilot to fly while on antidepressant medication and for a period of up to three months after cessation, if a pilot elects to be treated in this manner, he or she could be out of work for well over a year. In adopting this attitude,... the FAA tacitly forces a professional pilot with severe depression to make an agonizing choice: give up his career, or continue to fly without treatment.*

Who among us can afford to be without an income for possibly a year or longer? Is it any wonder that pilots who suffer from depression would rather mask and hide their symptoms than to admit the problem and face the additional stresses of loss of income and temporary, or possibly permanent, loss of their livelihood?

✓ *...the FAA has created a situation that is potentially much more serious: The traveling public may have their aircraft piloted by a person who is severely depressed but <u>masking</u> his or her symptoms – or a person who is taking medication on the sly – in order to keep his or her job. Under such circumstances, which flight will prove to be the last straw for the pilot who can see no light at the end of the tunnel?*

✓ *Another factor that may cause airline pilots to hide or ignore their problems and avoid medical help is the complex and sometimes adversarial relationship that exists between pilots, the FAA and airline management. Airline managers ask pilots to confide their innermost problems, while simultaneously threatening to take away their livelihood.*

✓ *Statistically, many pilots will likely suffer from depression at some point in their career, but may not seek treatment out of fear of losing their job. Experts say that it is quite possible for a pilot to mask the seriousness of his or her condition.*

Now let's look at some excerpts from *"Pilots Can Mask Mental Problems"* by Don Phillips, that appeared in the *Washington Post* on Nov. 22, 1999:

✓ *A pilot who is good at masking internal problems often can get away with lying about mental conditions, according to government officials and physicians who did not want to be identified because of the sensitive international implications of the Egypt Air crash.*

✓ *No one has revealed the details of co-pilot Gameel Batouti's last medical exam or any other medical or psychological records, but on the surface there is no indication that he would ever have been inclined to push an airliner full of people into a fatal dive.*

✓ *"I have seen a number of pilots develop problems after years of flying," said a senior federal official. "It can happen any time in a career."*

✓ *Aviation has wrestled with the question of suicide and pilot mental problems for decades. In a 1971 report to the Federal Aviation Administration, a research team led by Robert E. Yanowitch suggested that some accident investigations include a detailed "psychological autopsy" to determine why a pilot took actions that seemed self-destructive.*

✓ *...and noted that families sometimes go into denial and even destroy evidence such as suicide notes.*

✓ *"...the fact that the deceased may have made plans for the next day or week is not sufficient reason to rule out a simultaneous preoccupation with suicide or a suicide plan," the report said.*

✓ *The report also noted that it is not necessary for a person to be planning suicide to exhibit self-destructive behavior. Destructive impulses "ordinarily are well-controlled and most unconscious," the report said. However, these impulses can be brought to the fore and released under influences of mental stress, physical exhaustion, frustration, alcohol, drugs and other tangible and intangible agents.*

✓ *Many commercial pilots seem to have several stories of the sudden onset of odd behavior among their colleagues...*

The following facts were found on the *Telephone Counseling and Referral Service* Web site (*www.tcrs211.org*) in 2002:

✓ Fact: *Currently there are slightly more than 30,000 suicides annually (83 suicides per day; or 1 suicide every 17 minutes) with 12 of every 100,000 Americans killing themselves.*

✓ Fact: *Males complete suicide at a rate four times that of females.*

✓ Fact: *Suicide rates are the highest among the divorced, separated, and widowed and lowest among the married.*

✓Fact: *White suicide rates are approximately twice those of non-whites.*

Here are additional facts that can be found on the *National Institute of Mental Health* Web site (*www.nimh.nih.gov*)*:*

✓Fact: *Suicide is the 11th leading cause of death in the United States.*

✓Fact: *It is the 8th leading cause of death for males.*

✓Fact: *There are an estimated 8-25 attempted suicides to one completion.*

✓Fact: *The strongest risk factors for attempted suicide in adults are depression, alcohol abuse, cocaine use, and separation or divorce.*

These statements can be found on the *FAA Medical Virtual Flight Surgeon* Web site (*www.aviationmedicine.com*):

✓*For the pilot, crossing the threshold of using medication for psychiatric purposes disqualifies him for flying as long as he is on the medication, and until he is cleared by the FAA to return to flying after stopping the medication.*

✓*Pilots remain one of the most difficult groups to persuade to seek mental health assistance, even when they can barely function.*

✓ *Another major obstacle is fear of having to report any counseling or treatment to the FAA and permanently losing their medical certificate. This fear is unjustified in the vast majority of cases.*

✓ *Even if the counseling is for a personal psychiatric diagnosis and is reportable, it may not be disqualifying for flying. If both the counselor and pilot feel it is safe to fly AND no medications are required, the pilot may generally continue to fly and attach a summary from the counselor at the next medical examination.*

✓ *Counseling by clergy, or even your personal physician, is not reportable if there is no personal psychiatric diagnosis, no alcohol or substance abuse and no treatment with medications. Visits to Employee Assistance Programs (EAP) for conditions described above are also not reportable.*

✓ *Insurance company records are not releasable to either the FAA or to your employer.*

The following excerpts are taken from *"Depression - A Recoverable Stall"* by Glenn R. Stoutt, Jr., MD, Senior FAA Aviation Medical Examiner:

✓ *The bad news is that depression is now so common that it is called "the common cold of psychiatry".*

✓ *Between 10 and 20 million people in our privileged and affluent country suffer from it* (depression) *to the degree that they need treatment.*

✓ *One man in ten...will be affected* (afflicted) *by it at some time during their lifetime.*

✓ *loss of a loved one, loss of a job, financial problems, divorce, illness, alcoholism and drug abuse, unhappy marriages, and nowhere jobs can push a person into depression.*

✓ *The FAA does not presently certify persons who use mood-altering medication. The reasoning is twofold: the underlying condition that requires the medication and the potential adverse side effects from the medication itself.*

✓ *The good (?) news is that the FAA is willing to return virtually all clinically depressed pilots back to flying after successful treatment.*

✓ *Alcohol abuse is probably just an attempt at self-medicating feelings of depression.*

✓ *Many depressed people with hangovers jump out of hotel windows on Sunday mornings.*

✓ *Men just don't want to admit of anything that takes away from the macho image. Depression is thought of as a wimp disorder.*

✓ *Men may just tough it out until the Smith & Wesson cure seems the only solution.*

✓ *Harvard Medical School psychologist Dr. William Pollack said, "Men are limited pretty much to a menu of three strong feelings: rage, triumph and lust."*

✓ *Men have a tendency to self-destruct.*

I don't know about you, but the foregoing causes me a great deal of concern. I feel sorry for any fellow pilot who is in such terrible mental anguish that he feels that he must take his own life. However, given the above information, I don't want to be riding in the cabin of an airliner that is in the command of someone who has attempted suicide. It's our opinion that these unfortunate souls should be put on full medical retirement.

Also, we believe that if the airlines and FAA are going to allow pilots to fly passenger jets after they have attempted suicide, they owe it to the traveling public to tell them who these pilots are. If you knew that your pilot was or had been mentally unbalanced, would you allow the airlines to herd you into a locked, potentially dangerous guided missile that a suicidal pilot can use to surreptitiously take his own life—and the lives of his innocent passengers? Would any of the passengers on those fateful 9/11 flights have boarded their aircraft if they knew that a pilot bent on suicide was in command of the flight?

✈

Pilot Fatigue

Let's turn now to the issue of crew fatigue. I'm sure you will recall these quotes from our fictional story:

"...you saw the captain and the first officer for your flight make their way through the horde at the Jetway. They both looked very tired. It briefly passed through your mind that they appeared to be much too tired to be guiding a 150,000 pound jet through the night sky."

"The weariness induced by your grueling travel day had left you in no shape to think clearly, let alone to competently handle heavy machinery and make exacting, life-and-death decisions."

"By the time you saw him in DFW preparing to take command of the airplane that would wing you home, he was extremely fatigued and distracted. He was so fatigued and distracted that if he had been given a test for impairment, it would have revealed that he was more impaired than if he were legally drunk."

The issue of fatigue is not a new problem; it's been around since the beginning of time. It's a fact, the human body needs sleep to recharge itself. Fatigue affects our moods, personality, temperament, reasoning and decision-making abilities. If you don't believe that, just take a close look at any over-tired person; they illustrate this quite clearly.

Once again, let's turn to the FAA Aeronautical Information Manual for the FAA's guidance on this issue:

✓ *Fatigue continues to be one of the most treacherous hazards to flight safety, as it may not be apparent to a pilot until serious errors are made. Fatigue is best described as either acute (short-term) or chronic (long-term).*

✓*A normal occurrence of everyday living, acute fatigue is the tiredness felt after long periods of physical and mental strain, including strenuous muscle effort, immobility, heavy mental workload, strong emotional pressure, monotony, and lack of sleep. Consequently, coordination and alertness, so vital to safe pilot performance, can be reduced. Acute fatigue is prevented by adequate rest and sleep, as well as by regular exercise and proper nutrition.*

In 1998, the Battelle Memorial Institute issued a report on the effects of fatigue. The following highlights have been excerpted from the report:

✓*The massive literature on fatigue has identified a number of symptoms that indicate the presence of fatigue, including: increased anxiety, decreased short-term memory, slowed reaction time, decreased work efficiency, reduced motivational drive, decreased vigilance, increased variability in work performance, increased errors of omission which increase to commission when time pressure is added to the task.*

✓*A review of the literature that involved fatigue levels likely to be experienced by pilots suggests that a common fatigue symptom is a change in the level of acceptable risk an individual will tolerate.*

✓ *...fatigue caused subjects to engage in greater risk taking activity in an effort to avoid additional effort. This was also noted by two other studies, conducted in 1974 and 1976.*

✓ *Related evidence exists that fatigued workers are satisfied with lower performance and perceived errors go uncorrected.*

We all experience fatigue at one time or another, but still we often press on because we want or need to get a particular task done. That's when mistakes happen and errors occur. A single mistake or lapse in judgment may not cause disaster. However, very seldom is a single mistake ever made. More often than not, one mistake leads to another. It has been shown that this "error chain" frequently leads to an accident.

Pilots, as a rule, are disciplined, meticulous, conscientious and safety-oriented people. Their mission is to deliver their passengers from point 'A' to point 'B' in a safe and timely manner. Yet sometimes, their good judgment lapses when there are conflicts concerning the mission and fatigue is present.

As professional pilots, we are very aware of fatigue and its effects on flight crews. At one time, I even taught a class on the subject at a large provider of corporate-crew training. Although there have been trips we should have cancelled due to fatigue, for various reasons that are all too familiar to professional pilots, we didn't. One trip in particular occurred in the summer of 1999. Christine will tell you how it went.

At the time, we were a flight department of two. After a seven-hour duty day, we were released for a rest at 1830. That gave us eleven hours free of duty (three hours more than the minimum required break for airline crews) before the next morning's required report time of 0530. After four legs on the second day of the trip (three of which were in instrument conditions), we were released at 1130 for an afternoon layover. Our next report time was 1830 that evening. We grabbed a bite to eat and headed to the hotel for some "quick" sleep before our next report time.

We had seven hours in which to eat, sleep, shower, dress and travel to and from the airport. Trying to sleep during the day is almost impossible. The rest of the world does not sleep during the middle of the afternoon. Due to outside noises made by hotel employees and guests, our sleep was light and broken. If we got two hours of good sleep, we were lucky.

We reported back on duty at 1830 to begin the next set of flights. The second leg of the night was delayed almost two hours. This pushed back our departure to 2238. I was beginning to feel fatigued. The fourth and final leg began at 0115 with a ninety-minute flight to our final destination for the night.

I was so fatigued at this point that anything but sleep was impossible. Dave was not quite as fatigued as I, so he flew the leg. We should have cancelled the fourth leg of the trip that morning, but the boss was counting on the airplane being back home because we had flights scheduled for later that morning. We pressed on and completed the flight, reporting off duty at 0300. Had there been severe weather, an in-flight emergency or a tough operational decision to make on this last leg, would we have been able to safely handle it? We don't know.

Exactly eight hours after landing at our home airport, we were back on duty for another three-leg, eleven-hour duty day. We were lucky. We flew fatigued and nothing happened. Most owners of crew-flown airplanes acknowledge that crew fatigue exists and that it can be a problem. However, they tend to ignore the situation if it inconveniences their schedules.

This is only one of many tales of impairing fatigue that we could tell. If you'd like to hear more, you can go to our Web site *(www.aerospacetrust.com)*. Now let's see what others have to say about this ubiquitous problem.

The *Miami Herald* published an article by Martin Merzer in June, 1998 titled *"Many Pilots Catch Shut-eye on the Job":* Here are a few excerpts from the article:

✓ *Here's a problem that could keep you awake at night: Airline pilots are falling asleep on the job. How often? Fasten your seatbelts.*

✓ *Studies conducted by federal aviation experts and NASA suggest that one in seven pilots is nodding off in the cockpit. Experts say that's a conservative estimate.*

✓ *Bill Jordan, a former pilot for Miami-based Eastern Airlines, said most pilots are alert most of the time, but he has seen many colleagues fall asleep in the cockpit – and he has done it himself. "I don't think I ever talked to a pilot who hadn't," Jordan said. "We'd joke about it. We'd say, 'I'm checking my eyelids for light leaks'."*

✓ *The often-expressed concern: If one member of a two-pilot crew falls asleep, even during a flight's generally uneventful cruise segment, what happens if the other pilot dozes off or suffers a heart attack or otherwise becomes incapacitated just before an emergency?*

✓ *Mark Rosekind, a psychologist who conducted several pilot fatigue studies for NASA and the FAA says, "The general public doesn't understand that fatigue plays a big role in the system. You deal with this every single time you fly."*

✓ *Rosekind served for seven years as leader of the Fatigue Countermeasures Program at NASA's Ames Research Center in Northern California. The unit was established in 1980 at the request of Congress. He said fatigue is epidemic among airline pilots, even those who handle relatively short domestic flights. Many must awaken long before dawn to make their first flight, abbreviating their sleep cycles.*

✓ Rosekind: *"Right away, you're accumulating a sleep debt, one that can build until mental and physical response time deteriorates."*

✓ *Despite the candor of Jordan...most pilots are reluctant to speak about their experiences with fatigue.*

✓ *"Fatigue is certainly a significant safety issue in the flight environment," said David Neri, a research psychologist who runs NASA's pilot fatigue studies.*

✓ *In one notorious event during the 1980s, the dozing pilots of a transcontinental cargo flight overshot*

Los Angeles and flew for nearly an hour over the Pacific before controllers could wake them up and bring them back.

Fatigue in aviation is not a new problem. It is just an ignored problem. Charles Lindbergh (writing about his 1927 transatlantic flight) said, *"My mind clicks on and off. I try letting one eyelid close at a time while I prop the other with my will. But the effect is too much, sleep is winning, my whole body argues dully that nothing, nothing life can attain is quite so desirable as sleep. My mind is losing resolution and control."*

A report in a1998 *Miami Herald* article noted that human error has been responsible for seventy percent of airline accidents. The article concluded that drowsiness is an "error". Every pilot knows that fatigue can be deadly in the cockpit. Professional pilots experience it regularly. Why then do pilots fly when they are fatigued? How does their fatigue affect your safety? How can you tell if your flight crew is too tired to fly? What are the airline and Federal Aviation Administration (FAA) policies on fatigue? The answers to these questions will surprise you.

As we saw earlier, the FAA acknowledges in the AIM that, *"Acute fatigue is prevented by adequate rest and sleep."* Despite these words of wisdom, the following duty-day ruling was handed down to commercial air carriers in November, 2000. The FAA's Deputy Chief Counsel clarified 14 CFR 121.471(b), as saying that *"16 hours is the maximum time a pilot can remain on duty."*

Why was this interpretation so significant? Prior to this ruling, the airlines were able to "loosely" interpret the meaning of this Federal Aviation Regulation (FAR) as meaning that a pilot could be scheduled for a sixteen-hour duty-day and then be ordered to exceed that time limit if circumstances beyond the control of the airline (weather, mechanical, air traffic control or other delays) prevented them from completing their assigned flights for the day. This interpretation of the FARs could easily stretch a duty-day to eighteen or more hours.

On August 30, 2002 the FAA briefed the Air Line Pilots Association (ALPA) on its (the FAA's) implementation of the "Whitlow" interpretation which limits scheduled domestic pilots to a sixteen-hour duty day. Sixteen-hours, that's the equivalent of a double workday for most of us. The sixteen hours <u>does not</u> include travel time to-and-from the airport, or other off-duty activities. This is actual duty time, the time from reporting in at the departure station to the time the pilot checks out at the end of the duty day.

The FAA regulations governing crew rest is confusing to say the least. However, we can glean fron the FARs that the minimum rest period allowed between duty periods is eight hours. During this short period, pilots must travel to home or a motel, eat, sleep, shower, dress, and travel back to the airport. How much restful sleep do you think they are actually getting? Does eight hours meet the definition of *"adequate rest and sleep"* needed to avoid acute fatigue?

Captain Duane Woerth, president of the Air Line Pilots Association, stated in a press release on June 14, 2001:

> ✓ *A 16-hour day is hard enough for anyone, let alone a pilot, who must maintain his mental and physical faculties at top performance levels.*

> ✓ *A pilot who is on duty 16 hours has been awake at least 17 hours – and we know from scientific study that this produces an impairment in performance*

*equivalent to having a blood alcohol content
(BAC) of 0.05 percent. It is illegal for pilots to fly
with a BAC of 0.04 percent, because that
produces what the FAA considers to be an
unacceptable impairment to performance, yet the
airlines are content – no, let's make that adamant
– that their pilots be allowed to fly under
conditions worse than that.*

Studies have shown that tired pilots experience micro sleeps. What is a micro sleep? The Batelle Report cited earlier talks about this phenomenon. The report informs us *"The physiological drive to sleep can result in a micro sleep lasting a few seconds to a few minutes. During these lapses in information processing, subjects momentarily slip into a light sleep. This occurs with the eyes open and usually without the knowledge of the individual."*

Even when faced with scientific evidence that proves that a long day produces impairment equivalent to that of being legally drunk (as defined by the FARs), the airlines still continue to schedule flight crews for the maximum allowable time. "Why do they do that?" you may ask. The answer the airlines give is that it will impose an unbearable economic burden on them if they schedule their pilots for shorter duty days.

Instead of asking your flight crew if they're sober, perhaps you should ask them how long they have been on duty. It would also be nice to know how long they've been awake and how much sleep they had before reporting for duty. Unfortunately, the airlines will not let you know about these crucial factors that have a significant effect on the safety of your flight.

The reality of pilot fatigue is not new; neither are the rules that govern flight time and duty time. In fact, these rules date back to the 1980's. The current regulations have been fought over since at least 1996 and have just been *clarified* as of August 2002,(not changed).

In 1996, the Air Line Pilots Association (ALPA) submitted a report to Congress in response to the government's request for information. This report contained ALPA's position on the *"Notice of Proposed Rulemaking 95-18: Flight Crewmember Duty Period Limitations, Flight Time Limitations And Rest Requirements"*. This is the rule that was just clarified in Aug. 2002 that limits pilots to a SIXTEEN-hour duty day, and as we know, sixteen hours is much too long to be on duty. Here are excerpts from the ALPA report:

> ✓*The Airline Pilots Association (ALPA or Association) submits the following comments in response to the Notice of Proposed Rulemaking (NPRM) 95-18: Flight Crewmember Duty Period Limitations, Flight Time Limitations and Rest Requirements.*

> ✓*Over 60 years ago when the first professional pilots joined together to form a union, their main focus was not on higher wages or pensions, but on safety. Among the most egregious practice they faced was "pilot pushing", in which operators forced pilots to fly long hours in all kinds of weather to maintain the company's schedule.*

> ✓*While there are certain areas in the proposed rule that please the pilots, there are many areas in which it falls well short of the mark. Indeed, in the most basic and critical areas - including the standard flight limitation and the standard duty limitation - the Federal Aviation Administration (FAA or Agency) has ignored the scientific research and,*

in an apparent effort to appease the concerns of airline operators, has sanctioned a modern version of "pilot pushing".

✓*The NASA researchers recognized that airlines currently schedule 14-hour duty periods on a regular basis, but because of the likelihood of significant, performance-impairing fatigue, they specifically recommended the 10-hour limit, extended to 12 hours, only in the event of unforeseeable operational problems.*

✓*This [extended duty] limit is based on scientific findings from a variety of sources, including data from aviation, that demonstrate a significantly increased vulnerability for performance-impairing fatigue after 12-hours. It is readily acknowledged that in current practice, flight duty periods extend to 14 hours in regular operations. However, the available scientific data support a guideline different from current operational practice. This data indicate that performance-impairing fatigue does increase beyond the 12-hour limit and could reduce the safety margin.*

✓*In preparing our response to this NPRM, ALPA is concerned that the fatigue present in daily aviation operations will increase. We know that fatigue occurs. We asked our members to provide us with documentation of fatigue and that we received over 500 reports in response. Samples of these reports are included in Appendix B.*

✓*We urge you to read these reports and attempt to "wear the shoes" of these individuals who have so diligently taken the time and effort to write of their despair with the present system. Fatigue has no prejudice and knows no national boundaries.*

✓*These reports provide a unique opportunity for regulators to obtain an inside-the-cockpit view of the effects of fatigue in both short and long-haul operations.*

✓*The reports received from over 500 pilots in the United States also indicate that long flight times and duty times under the present rules contribute to many errors being committed on the flight deck. Albeit small errors, each mistake under certain circumstances could and have proved to lead to a major error, thereby creating a real potential for a serious incident or accident.*

In late 2002, Christine found the following reports of pilot fatigue on the ALPA Web site *(www.alpa.org)* in the site's *U.S. Pilot Reports* section. The report contained over 500 anonymous reports made by active airline pilots. Let's take a look at a representative sample.

✓*1300Z—Making a decent into Newark after an all-nighter from SFO* (San Francisco). *Capt. fell asleep after landing in a fatigued stupor. We were going to Gate 11; it was obvious we would not clear by over 18 feet on my (F/O) side. My marshaler finally threw up his hands for us to stop, but Capt. said no, his marshaler was indicating to continue.*

I got on the brakes and stopped the aircraft just prior to the wing contacting the parked DC-8's aft fuselage or horizontal stabilizer. Taxiing in, we never had a chance. On the subsequent flight into Chicago, the Capt. dozed off repeatedly enroute. On arrival, the Captain admitted he should not have flown trip because of fatigue.

✓ *(DC-9) 3-day trip with a day layover at DFW/Airport,* (Dallas-Ft. Worth). *Hotel between runways...report 0110 local to fly DFW-SHV-JAN-ORD.* (Dallas Ft. Worth,TX – Shreveport,LA – Jackson,MS – Chicago-O'Hare) *DFW departs 0210 to SHV. Short ground time SHV – depart to JAN; arrive about 0530 with depart for ORD at 0955 local. Flown numerous times, crew dozed at altitude DFW-SHV and almost over flew- happened to many crews often! Missing radio calls, clearances, altitudes etc. Crews were irritable, short-tempered, very ugly unsafe operation.*

✓ *We got into DEN* (Denver) *approx. 11:00 p.m. and I slept about 7 hours. Now I'm off all day at the hotel, planning a two leg all-nighter from DEN-SAN-ORD.* (Denver – San Diego - O'Hare). *There is a 2 hour sit in SAN then you get into ORD at 0500 (LCL)* (local time). *It was my leg. I hadn't slept all day because I just slept that night. So, I'm up for about 3 hours as I start the approach into ORD (marginal weather). When I got into OPS I literally could remember nothing about the approach or landing. Don't even know which runway it was. It's a legal rest period, but rest is impossible.*

✓ *After flying all night on a SEA-ANC-SEA turn,* (Seattle – Anchorage) *my flight arrived back in the SEA area at approx. 5:30 a.m. LCL. I had been awake almost 24 hrs. On my drive home from the airport (25 miles) I exited the freeway* twice *on the wrong exit due to extreme fatigue. (I had made this drive literally thousands of times previously.)*

✓ *This was the last leg of an 8-leg day trip. The previous two days were also 13 plus hour duty days with 8-9 legs a day. The weather was rain, fog thunderstorms. When we saw the runway it was at 100 feet AGL* (Above Ground Level). *I tried to line up straight but my reaction time was late, and my vision was blurred. I ended up in a drift to the left side of the runway 10-20 feet over the edge lights. The first officer informed me of this late into the occurrence, pushed up the power levers as he shouted to go around which we did. I am a 10,000 hour pilot with 8,000 plus hours as a Captain. I felt my skill and judgment was impaired by fatigue, since my experience had never been brought so close to an accident. In my opinion, a solid duty/rest regulation should have prevented my near accident.*

✓ *We were scheduled with continuous-duty overnights all month consisting of (3) periods of flying in a row with two days off between. These sequences consisted of a MIA-NAS* (Miami - ?) *with scheduled 6 hrs break then a MIA-TPA-MIA turn* (Miami – Tampa). *Report for duty at 2100 and finish next morning (scheduled) after MIA-TPA-MIA at*

1100. Because of the fatigue induced by this schedule, I almost ran off the end of a runway at MIA. The runway was shortened approx. 3000' for repair. I didn't take this into consideration when landing; this coupled with a slight tailwind, bad judgment, and poor landing technique from being so tired required that I use maximum braking and maximum reverse in order to stop the airplane.

We stopped about 10' short of the end of the runway. Additionally, the fatigue manifested itself in many other ways that month such as: poor pre-flights, poor situational awareness at times, non-compliance with proper procedures in the cockpit, missed radio calls, and deteriorating flying skills as detailed above.

✓*After landing I called dispatch to report times. I was unable to effectively converse with the dispatcher. I could not remember our landing and block in time, even though it was only 10 minutes ago. I was extremely disorientated and confused. I almost fell asleep on my drive home. Another employee of my company (a pilot) did fall asleep after a similar fatiguing trip.*

✓*I was up for over 24 hours by the time we started our final decent. We (crew) missed numerous radio calls...normal SOPs* (Standard Operating Procedures) *were not complied with due to our fatigue. Both myself and the Captain fell asleep enroute to BCN. (Barcelona). Thank God nothing out of the ordinary (weather or aircraft problems) occurred. This crew was not capable of performing* due to our fatigue. Stop this madness or you're going to have more bent metal & dead people.

✓ *The captain was flying...In the turn he had fallen asleep. I shook him gently and as he jerked awake for some reason, he tried to pull a fire handle to shut down an engine. So as I am taking the plane away from him and waking him up and talking to the tower and answering the flight attendant who is wanting to know why we are flying in a circle, while all of this is happening the captain is making a move to pull the fire switch and kill an engine. He fully awakens and all is OK.*

✓ *After 7 days in the Pacific, we fly all-night from Bangkok to Narita, have a short day layover, then fly all-night to Honolulu. Some or all of the crew passes out on that leg from fatigue. We are so tired by the approach and landing that our thinking and reaction time is similar to being drunk. If the weather wasn't consistently good in* HNL (Honolulu), *I'm sure we would have lost an airplane a long time ago.*

✓ *On duty all night trip. Dept. PIT SKD 2030,* (depart Pittsburg, Pa. scheduled 2030). *Due to Wx* (weather), *actual 2330, arrive HPN* (White Plains) *0045. To hotel 0130, to bed 0200, wake-up call 0445, van at 0530, take-off 0630, F.O.* (First Officer) *flying. Both very tired, on final to PIT. F.O. called for flaps 40, I reached over and shut down #2 engine. Fatigue definitely a factor.*

✓ *My wife dropped me off at the airport for a 0550 show-time. She also picked me up later that day after waiting for me for over 1 hour. Flying nearly 8 hours may be safe when things go right, but it is a dangerously long day when they don't. We had WX (weather) delays, mechanical delays, a line check, and more mechanicals resulting in 3 aircraft swaps. At the day's end I was so tired that I forgot my wife was to pick me up. I rode the employee bus to the parking lot. Walked around looking for my car for 20 minutes and figured that I had parked at the company's hangar. My wife spotted me. I had such an exhausting day that even after seeing her it took me a few minutes to realize why she was picking me up.*

✓ *Last leg to base after long day, little sleep time night before leg – Pittsburgh to Akron. Both crewmembers tired and forgot to do approach course almost landed with gear up. Caught it on final and got it put down in time.*

✓ *Captain and second officer misread fuel gauges and erroneously computed the wrong fuel total on a B727 flight from Pittsburg to Atlanta. Take off was made without catching the error. Return to Pittsburg was accomplished and refueling was accomplished prior to continuing on to Atlanta. Fatigue was a factor since this was the last day of a four day trip. FAA violated the captain and the 2nd officer with 90 days grounding.*

✓ *727 crew—Enroute to BHM (Birmingham, Alabama)—on a visual approach to runway 23, while the Captain was flying the approach, we over shot final at 2500' AGL. I looked at the Captain and saw that he had fallen asleep while flying the approach. Notes about the flight: 1) the Captain was a serious by-the-book professional. He was an excellent pilot, and Navy trained. 2) The Captain mentioned that he did not get much sleep that day. He fell asleep on the layover but something woke him up after about 1.5 hours and he could not get back to sleep. 3) The co-pilot & engineer each got about 6 hrs. sleep. 4) If you look at the duty times, you see us scheduled for an early go followed by an afternoon-evening layover and then an all night flight.*

The National Transportation Safety Board (NTSB) has listed pilot fatigue as a causal, or possibly causal, factor in many accidents. The report on American Airlines Flight 1420 that took place in Little Rock, AR in 1999 is probably the most well known.

Our fictional story is loosely based on American Airlines Flight 1420. The factors that are cited as causes for this flight are numerous. Crew fatigue, airline scheduling, deviation from Standard Operating Procedures, weather and pilot error all contributed to the crash. We believe that crew fatigue was the precipitating factor.

Let's look at the National Transportation Safety Board Report (#DCA99MA060) on the accident to see what the board had to say:

✓ *The National Transportation Safety Board determines that the probable causes of this accident were the flight crew's failure to discontinue the approach when severe thunderstorms and their associated hazards to flight operations had moved into the airport area and the crew's failure to ensure that the spoilers had extended after touchdown.*

✓ *Contributing to the accident were the* **flight crew's impaired performance resulting from fatigue** (emphasis by authors) *and the situational stress associated with the intent to land under the circumstances.*

For additional information on the Little Rock crash, or to view the entire report, you can visit the NTSB Web site *(www.ntsb.gov),* or the Air Line Pilots Association (ALPA) Web site *(www.alpa.org)* or you can go to our Web site at *(www.aerospacetrust.com)*.

The NTSB's conclusions support what we believe should be done to reduce the risks associated with pilot impairment:

1. Limit crew duty times to substantially less than what the current FAA regulations and the airlines adhere to. We believe that duty days should be limited to ten hours.

2. Provide realistic rest periods. These rest periods should be during times that pilots normally sleep or can sleep. Quiet and secure sleep facilities

should be provided. We recommend that rest periods should be a minimum of twelve hours long.

3. All pilots should be tested for impairment before every flight and before beginning landing approaches.

Now let's look at some excerpts related to fatigue from an article titled *"Despite Safety Fears, Rest Rules for Pilots Unchanged"*. It was published in the *Seattle Times* on July 24, 1999. It was written by Chuck Taylor, the *Seattle Times* aerospace reporter:

✓ *Tired airplane pilots have reported a variety of mistakes: landing at the wrong airport, landing without permission from the tower, flying too fast, flying at the wrong altitude during approach to airports.*

✓ *Pilots want to maintain strict limits on flight time and want more mandated rest, especially for night flying, which is particularly disruptive to the human body clock.*

✓ *...rules governing flight and rest time for passenger- and cargo-jet pilots remain unchanged after more than 15 years of reform efforts.*

✓ *Airlines are concerned about the economic impact of more restrictive rules.*

✓ *...fatal crash-landing of American Airlines Boeing MD-82 in Little Rock. The crew had been on duty for more than 13 hours and had flown more than seven of those.*

✓ *NASA also has conducted research on sleep that confirms what might seem obvious: Late nights, early mornings, long day on duty, working nights and multiple time-zone changes can make for poor decision-making or awareness in the cockpit.*

✓ *The heaviest workloads are before and during takeoffs and landings, the phases of flight when most accidents happen.*

✓ *However, reports from pilots – to NASA or through their unions – suggest they occasionally do fly when they shouldn't, even if the rules compel them to decline an assignment.*

✓ *...the captain of a Boeing 727 cargo plane told of landing at Oshkosh, Wis., instead of Appleton, 16 miles away. "My fatigue, resulting in loss of situational awareness, caused me to lock onto the first airport I saw." the captain wrote. "None of the three crew members realized they had landed at the wrong airport until they were on the ground."*

✓ *In another example, the crew of a regional airline's jet 'busted' their assigned altitude, as pilots call it, after the crew inadvertently accepted instructions from air traffic control to fly an approach that was not possible. In crowded airspace, adhering to altitude assignments is crucial to avoiding collisions. "We were tired." one of the crew members wrote in the report to NASA. "By the time this last leg was completed we had been on duty for over 14 ½ hours and had flown seven legs for a total block (flight) time of nine hours."*

And some related comments from the ALPA Web site *U.S. Pilot Reports:*

✓*Neither the Capt. nor myself got (little or no) sleep prior to this flying and both became extremely fatigued as the night wore on. The fatigue definitely affected our flying skills, directly affecting our judgment and response time. Both of us "nodded off" several times. I called the XYZ MEC* (union) *office the day prior to this duty period, inquiring what my options were if I felt too tired to fly this duty period. I was advised that if I felt fatigued I had the right to walk off the trip and request crew rest, but was told that I would, in all likelihood, be disciplined and be docked pay for which I would have to fight the company. ALPA* (union) *said they would back me but there would be consequences. In addition to discipline and pay, I would be required to be counseled by the chief pilot. This scheduled flying is absolutely unsafe. The line pilot is put in the uncomfortable and difficult position of flying a safe operation and being disciplined. It's not right. It's not safe.*

If the airlines won't do what is right and reasonable, let the court of public opinion enter the debate.

✓ *To make me legal...scheduling had to make me sit for 4 hours in the middle of the afternoon (due to hours scheduled in 24 provision of FARs). With trip as flown I flew 33.2 hours in 7 days. While taxiing out I could not remember my First Officer's name. Recognizing fatigue is extremely difficult, especially since the fatigue slows the mental process which would be used to recognize fatigue.*

✓ *We taxied clear of the active runway and the captain called for the after landing checklist. I inadvertently closed both fuel shut off valves instead of shutting off the fuel boost pumps. Both engines were shut down and we were towed into parking. It was my mistake but 12-1/2 hours and a short night's sleep the night before didn't help. P.S. Management doesn't care about safety; they just want to meet legal limits so they can't get sued.*

✓ *This was the 3rd day of a 3-day trip; the 3rd day involving 9 legs to be flown in an approximate 11-hour period. Mid way through the 8th leg (after having missed numerous radio calls & having to request repeats on several calls), the F/O (First Officer) exceeded the assigned level off altitude.*

We then first realized that we were both exhausted to the fatigue point. Being at an out station, facing the possibility of canceling the final leg & the repercussions of declaring fatigued, we flew the 9th leg to our domicile fatigued. Although I am ashamed to admit it, it is the norm among most all the pilots at XYZ. If you don't think 'continuous day trips' & 'reduced rest' trips are the norm, guess again.

These are <u>THE MOST ABUSED</u> of the FAA rules within the regional ranks. And our company has told us (point blank) that they have no intention of changing. While I know I'm fatigued, yes, I do fear reprisal by my employer if I cancel a flight due to fatigue.

✓*On duty all night, then given 8 hours during the day to get legal rest 4 days in a row (a normal regional schedule) on Day 5 last flight back to STL (St. Louis) 25 minutes after departure both F/O and Capt. <u>sound asleep</u>, auto pilot leveled at 16,000. Woke up when A/C (aircraft) entered convective activity (towering cumulous) and hit Mod to SVR (moderate to severe) turbulence with airspeed at redline, since climb power still set! No Exaggeration Whatsoever!!*

✓*Like most aviation-safety issues, the question of pilot rest comes down to how much safety the airlines and, indirectly, the traveling public, are willing to pay for. The shorter the hours, the more pilots on the payroll.*

This last statement alone should make you wonder just how much value you're really getting when you opt for that "cheap seat" price or the "red-eye special". You might be shaving more than just a few dollars off the ticket price. You might be rolling up your safety net as well.

Fatigue is obviously affected by the length of the duty day pilots are forced to experience. The FAA is the controlling agency for pilot duty times. I'm sure you will recall these quotes from our fictional story:

"They had been on duty for almost fourteen hours and would have to make it to El Paso within the next two hours to stay legal in terms of their duty-time limits."

"Surely, the airline and the FAA wouldn't allow someone as fatigued as these pilots appeared to be to fly tonight."

"In fact, the Federal Aviation Regulations allowed your crew to get up at a very early hour despite their personal biorhythms, and to then work a sixteen-hour, stress-filled day."

Like most government entities, the FAA is a large organization. As with all large organizations, changes often happen slowly. Slow is one thing, at a snail's pace is another. And it is often at a snail's pace that the FAA makes changes; even those changes that are clearly warranted by the facts and are of an urgent nature.

One of the roadblocks that the FAA faces in making changes is keeping the airlines happy. The airlines, through their various lobbying groups and generous political campaign contributions, wield an extraordinary amount of power in Washington. This power is often used to force the FAA bureaucrats to give the economic impact of an air-safety solution more weight than the safety of air travelers.

Excerpts taken from an article written in 2000 by Eric Malnic of the *Los Angeles Times* highlight this point. The article is titled *"FAA Is Slow To Address The Problem of Fatigue Among U.S. Pilots"*.

✓ *About 20 top Federal Aviation Administration officials sequestered themselves in a windowless Holiday Inn conference room three months ago to sort out a mess of their own making. "We're here because we're in big trouble." Nick Lacey, the FAA's director of flight standards service, told the somber group. "Jane Garvey (then the FAA Administrator) is in big trouble. ...All of you...all of us."*

✓ *Serious questions are being asked by the Congress and the White House – is this agency performing its duty on safety?*

✓ *Three days after a fatal American Airlines crash last year (1999) that raised questions about pilot fatigue, FAA Administrator Garvey had promised to rigorously enforce FAA rules designed to make sure planes are not flown by exhausted crews.*

Nonetheless, the FAA top brass had just found out that a major carrier with the worst record (of compliance) has not even started to enforce that rule. And, to make matters worse, it was American Airlines.

✓*American Airlines officials acknowledge that they were out of compliance until last month, but said safety was not jeopardized.*

✓*However, records and interviews show that the FAA, which regulates the U.S. aviation industry, has been slow to aggressively address pilot fatigue, which the government's own studies have portrayed as a widespread problem.*

✓*Despite calls from the National Transportation Safety Board, the FAA has not always ensured that major carriers were following the rules governing pilot work hours and rest periods.*

✓*The FAA has long been criticized for being too easy on airlines and failing to address known safety problems until a crash occurs.*

✓*Evidence has mounted for 20 years that fatigue is a hazard among commercial airline pilots.*

✓*Flight-crew fatigue has been identified as the cause of at least three major jetliner crashes in the last decade – two involving U.S. carriers – and as a factor in at least one more.*

✓*In government reports, pilots themselves said they sometimes nod off in the cockpit.*

✓*American Vice Chairman Bob Baker said the airline's noncompliance should have come as no surprise to the FAA. The agency, he said, had been* informed that American could not add the 200 pilots necessary to comply with the rules by the deadline last Dec. 12. An extension request by American was denied.

✓ The Air Transport Association, the airlines' trade association, contended as recently as a year ago that strict observance of the rules would add unnecessary costs and that pilot fatigue was not a significant problem. But the group called last month for establishment of clearer duty-time limitations to reduce fatigue-related risk.

✓ In 1998, the FAA said that these rules (duty-time limits) would be enforced vigorously.

✓ In 1999, Richard Rubin, an American pilot and a safety representative of the Allied Pilots Association, called for a Department of Transportation investigation, saying "the failure of the FAA to enforce current regulations regarding crew rest is an industry-wide problem.

✓ About a year passed before the FAA sent inspector Robert Cook to American Airlines' Dallas/Fort Worth home base to make sure the order was being carried out.

✓ The FAA refused to release a copy of Cook's report.

✓ But Lacey said the report concluded that Garvey's order wasn't being carried out. American was violating FAA rules requiring the scheduling of eight hours of uninterrupted rest for pilots.

✓ *Studies by the National Aeronautics and Space Administration and the Battelle Memorial Institute (a nonprofit research corporation based in Columbus, Ohio) concluded that a pilot should not be on duty more than 12 hours.*

In 1980, the NASA Ames Research Center created "The NASA Ames Fatigue/Jet Lag Program" (now the Fatigue Countermeasures Program). This program, which was jointly funded for many years by NASA and the FAA's Human Factors Research Program, was created to collect systematic, scientific information on fatigue, sleep, performance in flight operations, and circadian rhythms (the biological "time clock" that regulates the body's daily sleep-wake patterns).

Michael B. Mann, Deputy Associate Administrator, Office of Aero-Space Technology, National Aeronautics and Space Administration, in a hearing on pilot fatigue before the Aviation Subcommittee of the Committee on Transportation and Infrastructure, United States House of Representatives, August 3, 1999, testified:

✓ *Throughout the course of this outstanding research program* (the NASA Ames Fatigue/Jet Lag Program), *it has been evident that pilot fatigue is a significant safety issue in aviation.*

✓ *Evidence regarding the existence and extent of fatigue in aviation has been gathered from several different sources and environments, including aviation operations, laboratory studies, high-fidelity simulations and surveys.*

✓ *Studies have been consistent in showing that fatigue is an issue with complex, diverse causes and potentially critical consequences.*

✓ *The presence of fatigue has been acknowledged by flight crews for many years. Fatigue continues to show up in NASA's Aviation Safety Reporting System (ASRS).*

✓ *It should be evident that no single approach or "fix" can eliminate fatigue as an issue from aviation.*

✓ *A successful approach will attempt to maximize each individual component resulting in an effective overall program.*

There have been numerous scientific studies conducted on the issue of pilot fatigue, yet the FAA has decided that a sixteen-hour duty day for commercial-air-carrier crews is safe. The evidence would seem to suggest otherwise.

Let's take another look at the *Miami Herald* article written by Martin Merzer—*"Many Pilots Catch Shut-eye On The Job"*:

✓ *Nevertheless, it's common knowledge within the FAA and the industry that some pilots nod off on a regular basis.*

✓ *We're aware that it's happening, said David Catey, an airline operations specialist with the FAA. We're not quite sure what we can do about it.*

✓ *The FAA mandates maximum flying hours for airline pilots, generally 100 per month. It also mandates minimum rest periods based on a complicated formula that ranges from nine to 11 consecutive hours between duty shifts, depending on the preceding flight schedule.*

✓ *But many experts say that's insufficient, because those rest periods include travel time to and from hotels, hours spent eating, and the time necessary for hygiene and dressing.*

✓ *Those FAA restrictions also don't consider the cumulative effect of jet lag and sleep deprivation. In addition, the rest periods may not coincide with the pilots normal sleep cycle.*

✓ *Experts and union leaders say pilots need longer interludes between flights, and duty-tour limits that take into account the time spent preparing for flight.*

The FAA's response to these pleas was to clarify that a sixteen-hour duty day is the maximum. They didn't reduce the maximum number of hours that a pilot can be on duty. They simply clarified the regulation that was already in place—the one that everyone, except the airlines and the FAA, believes is not restrictive enough to ensure a safe flight operation.

In a government that is well-known for its ridiculous over spending and ever-present red tape, the simple and clear solution to the problem (reducing the number of hours in a duty day) is not even officially discussed. Is this logical? Could it be that the FAA's refusal to institute more-sane duty-time limits is a direct result of the airlines' lobbying efforts?

This ruling clarified the regulation, but it did not enforce it. On June 12, 2001, the Air Transport Association (ATA—the airlines' trade association) filed a petition asking that the FAA stay enforcement of the regulation.

The Air Line Pilots Association (ALPA), which represents thousands of pilots at forty-seven airlines in the U.S. and Canada, was strongly opposed. Captain Duane Woerth, president of ALPA at the time, had this to say about the ATA's petition:

> ✓ *I've looked at the ATA petition, and in a quarter-century in the airline business, I've never seen such a blatantly hypocritical collection of distortions and half-truths attempting to camouflage naked greed.*

> ✓ *First, the FAA is not acting unlawfully, as the airlines claim. What is unlawful is the continued flouting of this safety rule by the airlines, even after the FAA put the industry on notice with a clear delineation of how the rule is to be interpreted.*

> ✓ *Second, they have the nerve to hide behind public interest, claiming that enforcement of the rule will cause passenger delays. If passengers are looking for someone to blame, it would be the airlines with their cheeseparing attempts to get by without hiring enough pilots.*

> ✓ *They (the airlines)* have already gone to court once over the 16-hour rule, and now they're trying to trip up the FAA with administrative red tape.

✓ *If the ATA were really interested in promoting safety, they would support their pilots, not oppose them every step of the way.*

✓ *We've had it with their endless protestations that they want reform, that they want pilots to get adequate rest, that they want to do the right thing. Anyone who believes that after reading the ATA petition simply isn't paying attention. It's about money versus safety, pure and simple.*

How long had the airlines been able to avoid adhering to the sixteen-hour regulation? Although this regulation dates back to 1985, the airlines have misused and abused the sixteen-hour regulation via a loophole called interpretation. The airlines "interpreted" the regulation as meaning a pilot could be **scheduled** for sixteen hours and exceed those hours if circumstances beyond the control of the airline prevented them from completing their assigned flights for the day.

The FAA finally stepped up after **fifteen years** and clarified that sixteen-hours is the maximum a pilot can be on duty-period. This rule was clarified on December 20, 2000. However, the abuse didn't stop there. The ATA filed a petition on June 12, 2001 asking for a stay of enforcement. This tactic stretched out enforcement of the rule even further. The FAA briefed ALPA on its implementation on August 30, 2002. It took the FAA more than **seventeen years** to finally enforce the regulation. It's nice that the bureaucrats are finally implementing their own rule that has been on the books for almost **twenty years**. However, as we have seen, this antiquated rule simply does not provide the traveling public with the safety that it deserves.

✈

July, 2002 saw the re-emergence of another pilot-impairment issue that has perennially plagued the industry. Headlines proclaimed *"Pilots Face Drinking Charges"*, *"America West to Fire Pilots Charged With Drunkenness"*, *"Drunk Pilots Can't Help Airlines' Image"*, *"Pilot Resigns Amid Probe Into If He Showed Up Drunk For Flight"* and *"Passenger Escorted Off Plane After Making Sobriety Comment"*.

This isn't the first time public attention has been focused on drinking pilots. This has cropped up on-and-off for several decades. An infamous incident involving three Northwest Airlines pilots brought it into public view in 1990.

In that incident, the three pilots flew a Northwest Airlines Boeing 727 carrying fifty-eight people from Fargo to Minneapolis. Federal authorities were tipped off by an FAA inspector who had learned the three had been drinking heavily at a bar the night before their flight. The three intoxicated pilots were arrested.

On July 2, 2002, two America West pilots were arrested minutes before they were to take-off from Miami with one-hundred-twenty-four passengers on board. Breath tests revealed that both pilots had blood-alcohol levels above 0.08. It was their first flight of the day. Both received three DUI-related charges, including operating an aircraft under the influence.

America West cancelled the flight and told passengers that it had been cancelled "due to unforeseen circumstances". Granted, the pilots showing up intoxicated for a flight can be classified as unforeseen circumstances. However, didn't the passengers have a right to know that the pilots had been tested and found to be drunk? Isn't this a clear case of omission of a pertinent safety-related fact?

One week later, a passenger was escorted off another America West flight for making a remark about the pilots' sobriety. *USA Today* reported:

> ✓ *A passenger boarding an America West flight was escorted off the plane after making a remark about the pilots' sobriety, an airline official said Tuesday.*

> ✓ *The flight crew questioned the woman Monday about whether she was making a joke or an accusation.*

> ✓ *The woman was removed from the flight and taken to the airline's station manager where the comment was interpreted as an accusation.*

> ✓ *The pilots voluntarily also went to the station manager, and it was determined they were sober. No sobriety tests were given.*

> ✓ *The comment occurred one week after two America West pilots on a Miami flight were charged with operating an aircraft under the influence of alcohol.*

Neither the article nor the airline said how it was determined that the pilots were not impaired. How were the pilots deemed to be sober if no sobriety tests were given?

For a look at why pilots drink when they shouldn't, let's turn to the *Atlanta-Journal Constitution* of July 3, 2002 wherein we can find an article titled *"Pilots In The Air While Drunk Called Rare"*:

> ✓ *What could cause airline pilots to jeopardize their lives and careers – to say nothing of their*

*passengers' safety – by flying under the influence
of alcohol?*

✓*Lyle Prouse (who was the Northwest captain in that
infamous crew) says pilots who drink excessively –
just like spouses, drivers and others who do the
same thing – don't believe they are endangering
anyone.*

✓*Most airlines also have voluntary programs in which
employees can get treatment for drug or alcohol
addictions without giving up their flying careers.*

✓*The effects of alcohol become more pronounced at
high altitudes, and most airline cabins are
pressurized to 8,000 feet.*

On August 13, 2002, Christine found an article titled *"Airline
Fires Pilot Who Tests Positive For Drinking"* on the CNN Web site
(*CNN.com*). Here are a few excerpts:

✓*FORT WORTH, Texas (CNN): Mesa Airlines fired
one of its pilots after he tested positive for
consumption of alcohol before boarding his flight
from Little Rock, Arkansas to Charlotte, North
Carolina, an airline spokesman said Tuesday.*

✓*Spokesman Brian Gillman said that Capt. ...had
been with the company for two and a half years with
no previous disciplinary actions against him.*

✓*The captain has been terminated, effective last
night, Gilman said.*

✓*A screener thought he smelled alcohol on the breath of a [male] flight attendant and alerted authorities. When the police responded, they smelled alcohol on ...[the captain's] breath, but not on the flight attendant's, according to the police report.*

✓*All the crew members were taken off the plane and given Breathalyzer tests by the police, said FAA spokesman John Clabes.*

✓*Gillman said [the captain] was the only crew member who tested positive, but the crew's first officer was suspended from flying until the conclusion of the investigation.*

A look at how widespread this problem is, and what the FAA is doing about it, can be found in *"Pilots' Arrests Highlight FAA's Alcohol Concerns"*. It is an article written by *Los Angeles Times* reporters Eric Malnic and Ricardo Alonso-Zaldivar. It appeared on Monday, July 08, 2002. Here are a few excerpts:

✓*Federal records don't list a single commercial airliner crash that has been linked directly to drinking, but that doesn't mean professional pilots haven't been caught flying, or attempting to fly, when drunk.*

✓*After the Northwest Airlines incident, the FAA instituted random flight crew tests for alcohol and drugs, checking about ten percent of the country's 265,000 professional aviators every year. In* addition, the agency began perusing pilots driving records, looking for arrests for driving under the influence of drugs or alcohol.

✓ *Of the pilots subjected to the random checks, nine tested positive in 2000, nine more in 2001 and nine so far this year (2002).*

✓ *Arrests for driving under the influence led to the revocation or suspension of the pilot licenses of 230 professional aviators in 2000, and 220 in 2001.*

While the thought of having an intoxicated flight crew at the controls of your flight is cause for concern, there is a much greater, and more likely, danger that your pilots are fatigued. No one wants to fly with a pilot who is drunk. Why then does the traveling public (that's you) put up with the airlines' practice of forcing pilots to fly when they are fatigued?

If your flight crew is alcohol-free but fatigued, they may not be any safer than if they had been drinking. While this may seem to be a pretty bold statement, it has been proven to be a fact. It's been demonstrated through reports on aviation operations, laboratory studies, high-fidelity simulations, surveys and field studies.

Let's return to the Batelle Report cited earlier to see how fatigue can be worse than drunkenness. Here are a few excerpts from the report:

✓ *Reductions in task performance over time are also accompanied by an increased need to sleep, as shown by Lisper et al. (1986), who found that car drivers showed an increased likelihood of falling asleep after 9 hours of driving.*

✓ *The relative risk of an accident at 14 hours of duty rises to 2.5 times that of the lowest point in the first eight hours of duty.*

✓ *Askertedt (1995) reports accident risks to be threefold at 16 hours of duty, while Harris and Mackie (1972) found a threefold risk in just over 10 hours of driving.*

✓ *These levels of risk are similar to that associated with having narcolepsy or sleep apnea (Lavie et al.,1982) or a blood alcohol level of 0.10 percent.*

✓ *Wegmann et al. (1985) in a study of air carrier pilots, argued for a duty period of 10 hours with 8.5 hours or less of flight in a duty period.*

✓ *The research cited on duty period duration suggests that duty periods at or above 12 hours are associated with a higher risk of error.*

✓ *Samel et al. (1996) determined that many pilots begin night flights already having been awake more than 15 hours.*

✓ *Dawson and Reid (1997) evaluated performance after 17 hours awake and found that performance degraded to a level equal to that caused by a blood alcohol concentration (BAC) of 0.05 percent. At 24 hours, performance decrements were equivalent to that of 0.10 BAC. After ten hours of sleeplessness, the decline in performance averaged .74 percent per hour.*

✓ *Since the front part of the brain is responsible for analysis of information, judgment, planning, decision making, and the initiation of actions, it is not surprising that the NTSB found decision making abilities suffered with high time since awake.*

✓ *In a study of flight-crew involved major accidents of domestic air carriers during the 1970 through 1990 period (NTSB, 1994), one conclusion pertained directly to the issue of fatigue: Half of the captains for whom data were available had been awake more for more than 12 hours prior to their accidents.* Half the first officers had been awake more than 11 hours.

✓ *Crews comprising captains and first officers whose time since awakening was above the median for their crew position made more errors overall, and significantly more procedural and tactical decision errors.*

✓ *This finding suggests that fatigue may be an important factor in [air] carrier accidents.*

Now let's look at generally accepted effects of various levels of Blood Alcohol Content (BAC) on people.

1. <u>BAC of 0.02</u> (approximately one drink): Light or moderate drinkers feel some effect, usually warmth or relaxation.

2. <u>BAC of 0.04</u> (approximately two drinks in an hour): Most people feel relaxed, talkative and happy. The skin may flush. Fine motor coordination will be affected.

3. <u>BAC of 0.05</u> (approximately two drinks in an hour): First recognizable changes occur, with light-headiness, giddiness, lowered inhibitions and less control of thoughts. Restraint and judgment are lessened and coordination may be slightly altered. Driving is significantly more dangerous and should be avoided. DWI convictions occur at this level at judge's discretion.

4. <u>BAC of 0.08</u> (approximately three-to-five drinks in an hour): Loss of self-control. Crash risk greatly increased.

5. <u>BAC of 0.10</u> (approximately five drinks in an hour): A clear deterioration of reaction time and muscle control is present. Speech will be fuzzy and a general clumsiness will appear.

The Federal Aviation Regulations (FARs) Part 91.17, General Operating & Flight Rules, states:

> *No person may act or attempt to act as a crewmember of a civil aircraft:*
>
> *(1) Within 8 hours after the consumption of any alcoholic beverage;*

(2) *While under the influence of alcohol;*

(3) *While using any drug that affects the person's faculties in any way contrary to safety; or*

(4) *While having **.04 percent** [authors'* emphasis] *by weight or more alcohol in the blood.*

So what does all of this mean? The FARs state that a pilot is not to fly with a BAC of 0.04 or greater. The FAA obviously deems anything greater than this to be a direct hazard to safe flight.

At the same time, FAA regulations state that sixteen hours is the maximum an airline pilot can remain on duty. If a pilot can be on duty for sixteen hours maximum, then it stands to reason that he or she has been awake for at least seventeen hours. The maximum duty time does not take into consideration the time needed before duty for personal hygiene, eating or travel time to the airport. The time needed for these tasks can easily be two hours or more.

Studies have shown that the impairment experienced at the end of seventeen hours of awake time is equivalent to the impairment experienced with a BAC of 0.05. Therefore if your pilot has been awake for seventeen hours, or more, he or she is more impaired by fatigue than if he or she is drunk per the FARs.

Also, while a legally drunk pilot will "sober up" as time goes by, a fatigued pilot's performance will only deteriorate over time. Even when faced with scientific evidence that proves that a long day produces impairment equivalent to a pilot being legally drunk per the

Federal Aviation Regulations, the airlines still continue to schedule flight crews to the maximum allowable time, and the FAA sanctions it.

Why, then, is the flying public so concerned about the small percentage of intoxicated pilots while a more widespread threat to safety may already be at the controls? It seems obvious that the difference between being impaired by alcohol and being impaired by fatigue is that at least the drunk pilot will sober up; the fatigued pilot's performance has nowhere to go but down.

Instead of asking your pilot if he's sober, perhaps you should be asking him how long his day has been, how long he's been awake, and how much sleep he had before reporting for duty. If you don't know the answers to these questions, you are relying on false security to keep you safe. Aren't you convinced yet that false security is not really as good as real security?

You may still be wondering about the possibility of several of these safety-related factors coming together on a particular flight, as was the case in our story. Actually, this is the norm rather than the exception. If you read many aviation-accident reports (as we have), you will find that in almost every accident there was a sequence of misjudgments or poor decisions that led to the accident. Aviation professionals call this the "error chain".

Rarely is an accident caused by a single mistake. It usually takes three or more missteps (or "links" in the error chain) to cause an accident in today's aviation environment. Usually these subtle slip-ups are difficult to detect in the stress-filled, highly dynamic cockpit setting. The really interesting fact is that if any one of the links in the error chain is removed, the accident would not have happened.

Today's professional pilot training places a remarkable amount of emphasis on identifying these links before they form a chain that can lead to an accident. Formal protocols are taught that make it easier for pilots to first detect, and then deal with, the links.

However, undetected error-chain links appear to be the major cause of aviation accidents. We believe that the primary reason that links in an error chain go undetected is pilot impairment—both subtle and obvious.

Once again, I would like to tell you a personal story to illustrate this point. This is a tale about the only time that I have been in an airplane crash in the forty-four years that I have been flying. I had resigned from United Airlines almost one-year prior to the accident, but I had been doing a considerable amount of flying in conjunction with my business activities.

The story begins on a very cold December morning in Chicago. The weather was good in Chicago and at our destination, Springfield, Illinois. We planned to be back in Chicago by mid-afternoon. A business associate of mine was flying his airplane on the mission, and I was flying as safety pilot in the right-hand cockpit seat. Two other associates were riding in the cabin.

The flight was very important to me. Our group was in the process of acquiring the assets of the then-recently bankrupt Midway Connection regional airline. We were anxious to get to

Springfield, so we had agreed on a 0600 departure from Palwaukee Airport (KPWK) which is located in a Chicago suburb.

Since I was not the pilot-in-command for the flight (officially I was just a passenger), I had stayed out late the night before visiting with business associates and working on our acquisition strategy. I had also consumed a considerable amount of alcohol. I was also in the early stages of a very contentious divorce proceeding, and my personal financial situation was causing me a great deal of concern. To say that I was in a highly stressed condition would be putting it mildly.

Our flight to Springfield was uneventful. We spent all morning doing due diligence for the acquisition and negotiating with the president of the company. The meetings ran longer than we had anticipated. Instead of returning to Chicago by the early afternoon, we rearranged our day to leave Springfield in the early evening. By mid-afternoon, I could feel fatigue setting in. My activities of the previous night, the intensity of our meetings and the stress that I was under were beginning to wear me down. I was also very short on sustenance and very long on caffeine.

As the winter sun appeared to accelerate its descent to the western horizon, I received a telephone call from a friend and business associate. He was also an experienced pilot and a former top-level executive for United Airlines. I was trying to put a business deal together with the major aviation company he was now the co-chairman of. He was in Oklahoma City on business and he wanted to fly his company's corporate aircraft back home to Chicago. However, since he was getting up there in years, he had promised his wife that he would not fly the high-performance Cessna 421 alone. He wanted me to fly out to Oklahoma City (KOKC) and then fly back to Chicago with him as his safety pilot.

I wanted to help him out because I did not want him to fly alone at night and I obviously felt pressured to comply with his wishes so I could keep our business deal on track. Before I checked on airline seats from Springfield to KOKC, I informed my companions of my change in plans. The associate with the airplane we had flown to Springfield offered to fly me out to KOKC. He had business in Tulsa the next day, and he assured me it would not be an imposition for him to fly me to KOKC. Our other two associates decided to return to Chicago via KOKC. They were also former airline executives and they wanted the opportunity to spend a little time with our mutual friend on the trip from KOKC - Chicago.

We finished our meetings in Springfield and flew out to KOKC—it was after 2200 when we arrived. Needless to say, by this time I was extremely fatigued. However, all of us on the Chicago-bound flight had important meetings early the next day. The pressure was on us to fly to Chicago that night rather than take the more-prudent course of action of staying in Oklahoma City until morning. The weather was good in Chicago and along our route of flight. The flight looked like it was going to be a piece of cake. We departed for Chicago's KPWK airport.

The departure and enroute phases of the flight went smoothly. The night was star-filled and the air was as smooth as glass. While in cruise, we had a pleasant conversation as we consumed the sandwiches that our host had graciously thought to put onboard. All was well despite my growing impairment. My heightened level of fatigue was not a concern to me. At this point in my flying career, I had flown in this condition hundreds of times. Besides, I was not flying the airplane. This turned out to be a full-blown case of false security.

Chicago Center cleared us to begin our descent. The pilot-in-command pulled the throttles back and we smoothly altered our flight path from level flight to a gradual descent. As we passed through 17,000 feet, we encountered a very-thin cloud layer. It was so thin we could see ground lights through it. However, this stratum of moisture immediately froze to our windshields as we decended through it, totally obscuring all forward visibility. The captain turned on the windshield anti-icing system, and the ice was cleared from a five-inch-high horizontal strip near the bottom of his windscreen. My forward window on the right-hand side and most of his windshield remained opaque.

We came out of the bottom of the thin cloud layer into the clarity of a winter night. The whole Chicago area was spread out below us. It seemed as if we could see forever. The lights of the metropolis twinkled like a galaxy that had been affixed to the earth's surface. I relaxed.

We would be making a visual approach to 5,001-feet-long Runway 16—the longest runway at KPWK. This runway was equipped with an instrument landing system (ILS) that would assist my associate in his approach to a landing. The wind was virtually calm and this was my friend's home airport—he knew it well.

I asked the pilot if he could see OK out of the small patch of clear area at the bottom of his windscreen. He told me that it would be no problem for him to land the airplane. I did not inquire further into his ability to see, or into any alternatives that we should consider. My advanced state of impairment had induced a feeling of unwarranted well-being.

Approach Control rushed us into a visual approach to Runway 16. This was their normal procedure in a situation like this. They were very busy with inbounds to O'Hare, and they wanted us off their frequency. KPWK Tower was closed for the night since it was now well past midnight. We made the mistake of canceling our

IFR (instrument flight rules) flight plan before we had been radar vectored to the final approach course for Runway 16. When we left Approach Control's frequency, we were in a right-hand turn towards KPWK and I could clearly see the airport's beacon out of my side window. Things were going smoothly—I thought.

As we rolled out of our turn, the pilot said that he had Runway 16 in sight. I relaxed even more. Our descent to the runway went well. It wasn't until we were passing over the runway's threshold that I finally woke up.

I still couldn't see out of my forward window. My eyes were inside the cockpit monitoring airspeed and altitude. As we came over the end of the runway, the pilot raised the nose to flare for the landing and reduced the power on both engines. My peripheral vision told me that we were too high for this maneuver. Before I could react, the stall-warning horn was blaring and I could feel that we were sinking rapidly towards the runway.

I shouted "Power! Power!" and reached over with my left hand to shove the throttles up to go-around power. I grabbed the control yoke with my right hand. Our descent to the runway continued unabated since it takes a few seconds for the engines to reach high power. As the power came in, we hit the runway—hard!

We bounced back up into the night sky at a very-high power setting and a low airspeed. This is an extremely dangerous situation to be in. If the wing stalled, the airplane would in all likelihood roll over on its back and plunge into the ground. I pushed the nose over and, as it lowered, reduced the power slightly. My friend was also on the controls throughout these machinations. To this day, I'm not sure who was really flying the airplane. I suspect that we both were. Fortunately, we must have been making the same control inputs because I don't remember fighting him for control of the airplane.

When we hit the runway the second time, the left-main landing gear collapsed. We went off the left side of the runway and sledded over the snow. As the airplane gently decelerated, we went through the emergency shutdown procedures and braced ourselves for the sudden stop at the end our enforced sleigh ride. Thankfully, it never came. The snow allowed the airplane to smoothly stop at the end of its run.

I shouted "unfasten your seatbelts and get out!" (my old airline training coming into play), and we expeditiously exited the aircraft. As I stepped out the cabin door, I noticed a pool of liquid under the left wing and I smelled avgas. A thin wisp of smoke was rising from under the left wing. I shouted for everyone to get away from the airplane and took off running. We all stopped about two-hundred feet from the airplane and turned back to look at it. None of us had been injured, but the airplane appeared to be a total loss.

As we stood in the sub-zero night air looking at our crumpled bird, we took stock of the situation. The airplane was sitting in the middle of Runway 16, but it was pointed to the northwest—opposite to the direction in which we were landing. How could this be? We had gone off of the left side of the runway and plowed through the snow in a straight line. There was no way we could be back on Runway 16 unless we had made a complete circle. We were sure this had not happened.

Also, as we looked up the runway to the northwest, we could see that the northwestern-most two-thirds of the runway lights were out. On our approach, we could clearly see the runway lights along its entire length. Had we knocked the lights out when we went off the runway—was this possible? We were confused.

As we discussed the possibilities, we noticed an airplane with his landing lights ablaze approaching to land on Runway 16. He obviously couldn't see our crippled airplane on the runway. There was nothing we could do but watch. The airplane landed and continued its course towards the crashed Cessna. As his landing lights illuminated the crash scene, the pilot applied full-reverse thrust and stood on his brakes. He came to a stop about one-hundred feet from our airplane. As if nothing was unusual, he made a left turn and taxied to his hangar.

We made the quarter-mile trek to my friend's hangar through the frigid night. For the entire distance, we discussed what had happened. We still couldn't figure out how we ended up back on Runway 16. When we got to the hangar, we called the local police and the FAA to report that our crashed airplane was sitting on Runway 16.

Several hours later, over steaming cups of coffee, we finally sorted out what had happened. The error chain was initiated with our fatigue and high stress level. I was really in no condition to be part of a flight crew (I was officially just a passenger). My friend was also fatigued from his long day of meetings in Oklahoma City. The next link in the error chain was obviously the accumulation of ice on our windshields and the small clear area that was provided by the anti-icing system. We added a link by not thoroughly investigating our options after the window iced over (For example, we could have decided to land at O'Hare.).

The rushed approach that we blissfully accepted from Chicago Approach added to our problems. As it turned out, we realized that when my friend had said that he had Runway 16 at KPWK in sight, he was really looking at Runway 12. It appeared to be the longest runway on the airport (as Runway 16 in reality was) because two-thirds of the runway lights were out on 16. Runway 12's alignment is only forty-degrees different from Runways 16's. This difference in alignment was very difficult to detect at night on a visual approach. Also, since KPWK tower was closed, the runway-light outage was not reported to us.

The pilot's belief that he had Runway 16 in sight led him to focus on the visual picture rather than rely on the ILS for Runway 16. If he had used his instruments for the approach, we would not have lined up with the wrong runway. The final link in the error chain was forged when the pilot raised the nose to flare for the landing. The small area that he had to see out of showed him only black sky when the nose was raised. This caused him to lose spatial awareness at a very critical time.

When we finally deduced that we had landed on Runway 12 instead of Runway 16, the mystery of our ending up on 16 was solved. We had gone off the left side of 12 and our path over the snow led to Runway 16. How we managed to stop on the runway after sliding over the snow for several hundred yards, is still a mystery.

As it turned out, it was fortunate that the left-main landing gear collapsed instead of the right. Had the right failed, we would have gone off the right side of Runway 12—and into several parked airplanes and a hangar. I doubt that we would have walked away from the crash unscathed if that had happened.

I hope that you are now convinced that many things can come into play on a single flight to cause an accident. I have, of course, replayed this accident in my mind many times over the years since that night. I have decided that if only one of the links in this error chain were removed, the accident would not have happened. In my opinion though, impairment was the demon that precipitated the event and it was impairment that caused us to disregard the subtle warnings that things were not going as they should.

Pilot impairment—in its many manifestations—is, in our opinion, the biggest threat to air-carrier safety facing us today. Fatigue is clearly the most serious problem, but emotional distress, operational stresses and pilot suicide are also serious concerns that need to be addressed immediately. The airlines are focused on their bottom lines. The FAA seems to be ensnared by the power of the airlines' lobbyists. Who then will do something about it? The answer can be found in Chapter 13.

Chapter 13: "Ascending Unto Heaven"

"It will free man from the remaining chains,
the chains of gravity which still tie him to this planet.
It will open to him the gates of heaven."

> *Dr. Werner von Braun,*
> *on the importance of space travel,*
> *1958*

In the preceding chapters of this book, we have endeavored to provide you with the information that you need to make up your own mind about the differences between *false security* and *real security*. We hope that we have also supplied you with a new awareness of the major safety and service issues that are facing the airline industry today.

In grammar school, Sister Mary Louise always told us to never present a problem unless we could offer a solution. In our story about Air Travelers' Heaven, we offered some solutions to the problems facing modern air travelers, albeit in a fictional form. In this chapter, we'll reveal to you some of the real things that we, and others along with us, are doing to build a stairway to Air Travelers' Heaven. You'll also learn how you can join with us to accomplish this task

In early 2002, Christine and I founded **The *Aerospace Trust*** (TAT). TAT is a non-profit charitable trust that we set up to foster aerospace education, research and development. TAT is the vehicle we are using to further our goal of improving air travel. We currently have several initiatives under way that we believe will have a significant impact on the way we all fly. The TAT Web site at *www.aerospacetrust.com* provides more information about these initiatives.

The *Aerospace Trust Press* (TATP) is a division of TAT. It serves as our publishing arm. This book was published by TATP, and we have a new book in the works, *"The Mission"*, that will go into much more detail about the aerospaceplane and off-earth migration. It is scheduled for spring-2003 publication.

The TAT initiative that we have launched to improve the current air-travel system is ***Air Travel Partners*** (ATP). I'm sure you remember reading about "Air Travelers United" in the story. It has now come to life as ATP. ATP is a non-profit membership organization. We have great confidence that ATP will be successful where others may have failed. As Noah said in the story, "...sometimes you have to fight a battle more than once to win it."

We believe that we can change the U.S. air-transportation system for the better by bringing together air travelers who sincerely want to improve it. Our best estimate is that there are over 100 million air travelers in the U.S. Just imagine what we can do if even a tiny fraction of that number unite to improve the air-transportation system for all of us.

This is not revolutionary thinking. AARP (formerly known as the American Association of Retired Persons) was founded in 1958 on the simple belief that the collective strength of their membership would enable them to serve the broader community and improve the quality of life for people as they get older. Today, AARP has over 35 million members and it can point to many aging-related government policies that it has had a major impact on. We have been members for over five years.

AARP has amassed its clout by offering memberships that are reasonably priced while providing its members with high-value services. It then makes available to its members quality information and education on the issues that the membership is interested in. Then mechanisms are employed (magazine, Web site, etc.) that facilitate the sharing of this information and the individual member's position on the issues. The membership then aligns itself by going through a process that results in an AARP position on the issues. This focused power is then concentrated on the changes they want to make through legislative, legal and consumer-advocacy campaigns on the national, state and local levels.

We believe that this model will serve us well in our quest to increase the safety, speed, convenience and comfort of the airline system in this country. A little back-of-the-envelope calculating will show you what we mean.

Remember those approximately 100 million air travelers in the U.S.? What if only 35% of them had the gumption to throw a very modest amount of money, say $25, at a possible solution for their air-travel frustrations and concerns?

They would do this by becoming ATP members. If we multiply those 35 million members by a $25 annual membership fee, we can see that ATP would have revenues of $875 million each year. This would be a very-impressive war-chest with which ATP could implement very-effective legislative, legal, public awareness and consumer advocacy campaigns. With this kind of funding, ATP can ensure that air-travelers' rights are not just given lip service by the government and the airline industry.

Money talks in our society. And so do votes. If ATP can amass a membership base that is similar to AARP's, the financial and voting power at its disposal will certainly be able to force the government and the airline industry to make the changes that will provide us with a faster, more-convenient, more-secure and safer airline system in this country.

After all, we, the users of the air-transportation system, should have the most say as to how that system serves us. We pay for it. As it stands now, government bureaucrats and airline managers decide what level of service we get with almost total disregard for our opinions and demands.

As we write this book, ATP has several founding members. If you see the wisdom and logic of what we're doing, we would like to invite you to go to *www.aerospacetrust.com* for more information. We're hoping that we can count on you to join us in our fight for friendlier skies.

Together, we can solve the problems that we have been looking at in this book. Most of them have been around for a long time. If you do not work in the aviation industry, you may not have been familiar with the details. However, I'm certain that you were at least vaguely aware of most of the issues before you read this book.

So if they've been plaguing us for some time, how are we going to fix them now? The answer, my friend, is probably simpler than you may think.

As we pointed out in the earlier chapters, we believe that there are good, viable solutions to all of the problems that are keeping us from having the kind of air-travel system we would like to have. Most of the solutions will increase the cost of a ticket, but not by much. The solutions are well within reach of our current economic capability.

For example, we have learned that pilot fatigue has a remarkable impact on air safety. We believe that by reducing an airline pilot's flight schedule to pre-deregulation levels, accidents due to pilot fatigue would be greatly reduced. Today's airline pilots fly around 80 hours per month. Before deregulation, they flew approximately 40 hours per month. If you are going to cut pilots' schedules in half, then you'll obviously need twice as many pilots.

There are approximately 100,000 airline pilots flying in the U.S. today. Therefore, we would need 100,000 more airline pilots if all 200,000 are to fly 40 hours per month. I'll take a wild stab at the average airline pilot's pay. New-hire regional-airline copilots are paid around $25,000 per year (including benefits). The top captains at the major airlines pull down upwards of $250,000 (including benefits). There are many more modestly compensated copilots than top-paid captains. So, let's guesstimate the average at $100,000 (including benefits). To pay and benefits, we must add training costs. A good guesstimate is $20,000 per year per pilot.

Our 100,000 new pilots will therefore cost the airline industry an additional $12 billion per year. Approximately 670 million airline tickets are sold each year. If a "safety surcharge" of $18 per ticket were applied to this increased cost, then it would be entirely covered. Do you think it's worth an extra $18 per ticket to have well-rested, stress-reduced pilots at the controls of your flight? We do, and we believe that there are many others who would agree.

This is just one example of how "thinking outside the box" can solve a significant safety problem. We can apply this kind of innovative thinking and our collective power to the other problems plaguing modern aviation to secure for ourselves a vastly improved air-transportation system.

We're also taking a more direct approach to some of the problems we have looked at. This approach involves the establishment of an alternative to airline travel. Of course, this alternative must be affordable by a large segment of the current traveling public. And it must make air travel in the U.S. faster (in terms of portal-to-portal time), more convenient, safer, more secure and more enjoyable. We knew from the start that we would have to invent a new business model for this solution.

However, we looked to proven business models for guidance in this case too, just as we did when we chose the AARP model for ATP. Our model incorporates positive elements of several aviation businesses—airlines, aircraft-charter operators, corporate flight departments, fractional-aircraft-ownership programs and fixed-base operations. We are now in the process of launching this new venture. *"AvWorld"* is the name Christine coined for the company.

We have a twenty-year business plan for *AvWorld*. Our near-term goal is to set up the alternatives to airline travel that were presented in the story. And then to expand upon these successes until we are in a position to order a fleet of aerospaceplanes. If you would like more information about *AvWorld* and what it can do to satisfy your air-travel needs, simply go to *www.aerospacetrust.com* and you'll find a slice of Air Travelers' Heaven waiting for you there.

If you thought the ideas in the story about routinely going to the moon are too "far out", you might want to skip this section. However, we know that at least half of the readers of this book are eager to find out about how we're going to make human settlements on the moon a reality within the lifetimes of most of us who are alive today.

As Noah told us in the story, the survival of the human race depends upon establishing, as soon as possible, the means to routinely leave this planet. We believe that the establishment of settlements on the moon will provide the driver for the acquisition of this capability within our lifetimes. See if you can agree with the following logic.

Approximately one-third of the people on this planet, 2 billion people, live in the "developed world". These are the folks with the education, information and financial power to make human settlements on the moon a reality.

We believe that at least ten percent of them, 200 million people (In all likelihood, this number is probably closer to 1 billion.), think that we should establish, as quickly as possible, the means for humankind to routinely leave and return to this planet. And we believe that given the state of modern communications, we can bring these people together in an AARP-like organization.

Let's do another back-of-the-envelope calculation to see what the financial power of this group might be. If those 200 million believers pay annual dues of just $25, then $5 billion dollars per year would be available to facilitate the achievement of our objectives. And if those 200 million people were to invest an average of only $25,000 each *over the next twenty years* in profit-making ventures that were going to actually build the infrastructure that will take us to the moon, then these companies would have

$5 trillion in working capital to employ. We think this magnitude of financial power will be sufficient to get the job done.

We have established **The Outplan Society** (TOS) to bring these people together and to focus our collective financial and intellectual power on the goal of establishing lunar settlements within our lifetime. TOS is a membership organization that is modeled on ATP and AARP. It will provide quality information and education on the "why" and "how" of lunar development.

TOS will use innovative mechanisms to facilitate the sharing of this information. Individual member's positions on the issues related to settling the moon will be shared and discussed through web-based channels and periodic conferences.

When the TOS membership is aligned on the issues, legislative, legal and public-awareness campaigns will be employed to help shape the debate over our society's priorities as they relate to space travel. TOS will also provide leadership for the broader community of individuals who want to develop specific plans for leaving the planet as soon as possible.

TOS may seem to be a little far out to you, but someone has to do it—ensure the survival of the human race that is. The people of a much-less-populous and less-prosperous United States took humankind from no manned-spaceflight capability to routinely sending scouts to the moon in less than a decade.

The people of a much-more-populous and ever-richer planet can surely accomplish the goal of settling the moon in two decades. All we have to do is unite, achieve alignment and focus our collective power on the things that need to be done. We don't know about you, but we're betting on the survival of the human race.

As I am always ready to say, "The meek shall inherit the earth. The rest of us are leaving."

If you would like to find out how to join us in this adventure, all you have to do is visit the *www.aerospaceturst.com* Web site. We believe that we all owe it to ourselves and our descendants to do everything we can to ensure the survival of the human race.

Even if Air Travel Partners, AvWorld or The Outplan Society don't appeal to you as vehicles for providing the benefits we have talked about, we would still like to hear from you at *www.aerospacetrust.com*. If you have a better idea for improving the way we fly, please share it with us and our fellow air travelers.

Whether or not you agree with us on the ideas and issues contained in this book, we would like to ask you to pass the book on to someone else. Don't let it sit in a pile collecting dust where it doesn't do any good for anyone. Give it to a fellow air traveler, a coworker, a loved one who travels a lot, a library or simply leave it somewhere. In any case you can register the book at *BookCrossing.com* and have some fun as you see where it goes and who reads it. The important thing is to spread the word about what is really going on in the airline industry and what we can collectively do to improve the way we fly.

"Post-Flight Briefing"

"You define a good flight by negatives:
you didn't get hijacked, you didn't crash,
you didn't throw up, you weren't late,
you weren't nauseated by the food.
So you're grateful."

Paul Theroux

      I would like to personally thank you for having joined us on this flight of fancy and reality. I sincerely hope that you have enjoyed this trip and will decide to join us in our efforts to change the U.S. air-travel system. We believe that together we can make air travel safer, faster, more-convenient and more-enjoyable.

Before we say "happy landings", I would like to introduce some of the other crewmembers behind our vision of Air Travelers' Heaven:

◆ **_Mr. John Courtney_** has been vital to making this book a reality. He made a significant financial contribution to its production and marketing, and he made many editorial suggestions that were incorporated into it. John has contributed many hours to the development of our shared vision of a better way to fly.

John has enjoyed a forty-year aerospace career in the areas of new technology and major new government program initiatives. He was a pioneer in the initial development of military satellites for communications and intelligence acquisition and he continues to consult on satellite system designs and operational controls. His original operational concepts are still utilized by the government to provide operational control of unmanned satellites.

John and David have worked together for many years. Their first aerospace venture was the establishment of a United Airlines-Lockheed team to pursue the first NASA Space Shuttle Processing Contract.

◆ **_Steve Caler_** (CEO of Caler&Company—Akron, Ohio) has been a believer in this book from the beginning. Steve designed the cover and made numerous editorial and design suggestions. Steve gave freely of his extensive marketing expertise to help us get this book out to you. It was through Steve's creative planning sessions that the title "_False Security_" was chosen.

◆ *Mary Larrabee*, a copy-writer and editor, has contributed her time and talents to the review and editing of this book. Mary has believed in this book since its inception. In addition to her time and talents, she has generously contributed her moral and financial support to bring *"False Security"* to you.

◆ *Jason Koch*, David's son and a graduate student at Northern Illinois University, contributed his time, talents and technical support to the creation of the book. It was through Jason's computer expertise that the layout for the book and the creation of The Aerospace Trust Web site were possible.

◆ *Pat Worden*, *Steve Wheeler* and *Bob Scalfaro* graciouslyreviewed early editions of the book and provided valuable feedback.

David and I are looking forward to personally meeting you as we travel the country promoting *"False Security"* and attending Air Travel Partners functions. Of course, you won't find us in an airline terminal. You'll have to watch for us at your local general-aviation airport where we'll be landing in a private aircraft.
Until then —

Happy Landings,

Christine Koch

For more information

or

To order additional copies of

"*False Security*"

Visit our Web site at:

www.aerospacetrust.com

Quantity discounts available